To: Major
Moore, USMC (Ret).
A scholar, Warrior
Marine, and defender

WMD Attacks
on America

of our nation, I am Honored
to send this book to
you and Hope it proves
to be Worthy of review

By

Major Frank C. Stolz, USMC (Retired)

Very Respectfully
Submitted

Frank C. Stolz

P.S. Sir Take care
God Bless, Semper Fi.

About the cover: The American flag is displayed with the union down as a signal of dire distress in instances of extreme danger to life or property.

Dedication

This book is dedicated to all the enlisted men and women of our armed forces, both past and present. In my military experiences, I have witnessed that they always carried the heaviest loads and fought the hardest battles, and yet always cared for the welfare and safety of their companions. Many had little in the way of a good or proper schooling; most had little in the way of worldly goods, and few received the awards they so justly deserved. Yet they gave their all when asked to do so, and asked for so little in return. They, to me, will always be the true and unsung heroes of our nation's wars and defenses, and I, for one, shall never forget their bravery, their loyalty, and their honor, to an oft-unappreciative nation.

Major Frank M. Stolz, USMC (Ret.)

www.WMDTerror.com

Acknowledgments

After the Anthrax scare in Washington D.C., and deaths of the 9/11 Towers victims in New York City, I decided to check our government's plans and advice for civilians dealing with possible future incidents of this nature. Most people, like my own family members, are neither medically or militarily trained, so my original objective was to provide information and advice to family members.

I was astounded, as I scanned the U.S. government web sites, to learn they only provided information on these WMD subjects to first responders and the military. Even that information was woefully lacking in specifics. When I began to write the WMD document for civilians and family members, I was very lucky to obtain the assistance of my good friend, CWO-4 Jim Mulloy, a highly decorated and knowledgeable Marine. Together we prepared the non-fiction second portion of this book. We initially published it online and also sent copies to our troops, who in turn sent them to their family members before the start of the recent war in Iraq.

Because that portion of this book is somewhat technical and dry, we knew many would just scan it, but few would completely read it. Many people do not want to believe or accept the consequences of being unprepared for such surreal and horrible events.

That original WMD document was later the inspiration for the contents of the fictional first part of this book. However, since the initial writing some of the events and the national and terrorist alliances presented herein have in fact occurred and is now a daily part of our headline news.

While I have dedicated this book to all the enlisted members of our military forces, I would also like to acknowledge my former roommate and best friend 1st Lt Larry Taylor, USMC, of Pueblo, Colorado, KIA 1965 in Vietnam.

I do not have the space to list all the casualties in the units I commanded but they know they are in my thoughts and prayers. They include the men from 3rd Platoon, Fox Company, 2nd Battalion, 3rd Marines; 3rd Platoon, Alpha Company, 1st Battalion, 1st Marines; and several years later, Fox Company, 2nd Battalion 26 Marines.

I know reading an extended Acknowledgements page is the something many serious readers often ignore. In general, people do not know or care about some author's agent, publicist, or publisher. However, I do hope you will stay with me and read further.

Authors like Tom Clancy could not get a major publishing firm to even look at his book "Red October", and only through the pleading by some senior Navy Officers with the Naval Institute staff was the book ever published. Fortunately, President Ronald Reagan got a copy and liked it, which also helped create visibility, and enabled the book to gain popularity and later become a successful movie as well.

Likewise, Author John Grisham's first efforts were ignored by major publishers, and I have read and heard that he had to sell his first books out of the trunk of his car! Similarly, even Edgar Allan Poe had to print his own books, as publishers would not consider his works during his lifetime.

One has to wonder who continues to make these unbelievable misjudgments. New authors normally need not apply for a review, as in the vast majority of cases major publishing firms will not consider their works. Thus, new authors must rely on self-publishing or print-on-demand firms, who take their money up front and often leave the author's to their own devices for promoting and selling their books. I took that route with the first Edition of this book. Now I have become a self-publisher for the E-Book and for the printed version of this revised Second Edition.

However, this project could never have been completed and published without the generous time and efforts of Bob Rohrer and Brian Follas, who together created my website, the new cover page and other helpful additions to the book. I could never have afforded such an elaborate website much less a new cover – that is, had they not given so kindly of their time, efforts, support, and professionalism.

Strangely, Bob Rohrer and I were once Marine Corps Corporals at about the same time. He went on to a career as a successful Marketing and Sales Executive for major US. Firms, and now works as a Marketing Consultant. He can be reached at www.BobRohrer.com

Brian Follas is a very skilled web developer, visual designer, writer, and programmer who accomplished the design of my website, the production of the E-book, and the cover design of my new, soon to be available, hard copy version. He also helped me a great deal with other time-consuming computer issues. Brian is available to help others with their Web development objectives and he can be reached through his website at www.excomedia.com.

If this 2nd Edition becomes successful in informing and educating the American public on WMDs as well as Self-Protection and Home Remedies, then much of the credit belongs to both Bob and Brain. I offer a hearty Thank You to them both for a Job Well Done!

Major Frank C. Stolz, USMC (Retired)
October 2005, Round Rock, Texas
www.WMDTerror.com

"When you look out at the world from Vienna or Stockholm or Manchester and search for something to deplore, what do you see? You see Russia spiraling down into dictatorship after a brief interlude of struggling democracy. You see North Korea, arms salesman to the world's criminals, boasting of nuclear capability. You see genocide in Darfur [Sudan]. And of course, you see the ghastly face of terrorism in Madrid, Bali, New York, Washington, Tel Aviv and most especially Baghdad, where terrorists grab and behead innocent Americans and Europeans, and proudly videotape their savagery. But where do many Europeans focus their wrath? On the United States. ... There is something sickly about the European approach to the world."

-- Mona Charen, commentator, 2004

Cast of Characters

The Americans

- John Warrington (Democrat), the new American president
- Daniel McLaughlin (Democrat), Warrington's Vice President
- James K Matthews, FBI Special Agent to the White House
- Ed Pickings, the CIA Liaison Officer to the White House
- U.S. Army General Jonathan Paxton, JCS Chairman and former Chief of Staff of the Army
- Admiral Wayne Bennett, Chief of Naval Operations
- General Harold Robinson, Chief of Staff of the Air Force
- General Thomas Guy, Marine Corps Commandant
- Representative Barney Albertson (D-Kansas), Speaker of the House of Representatives
- Senator Susan Pelerine (D-Texas), the Senate Majority Leader and President Pro Tempore
- Alan A. Thompson, newly-appointed head of the Department of Homeland Security
- Dianne Epstein, Director of the CDC
- Maynard Johnson, Director of FEMA
- Linda Rivers, Director of the U.S. Red Cross Agency
- Brigadier General Carmine DeBona, Chief of the U.S. Army Medical Research Institute of Infectious Diseases
- John B. Kelly, National Security Agency (NSA)
- Ralph Cutting, the Chief of Staff
- Kathy Burgess, the speech writer

- Erika Shultz, the Press Secretary
- Phillip Mogates, the Head of the Secret Service detail
- Major Jim Stone and CWO-4 Frank Monroe, two older retired Marines and old buddies from the Vietnam War

The new Chinese leadership

- Lai Ming Qian, and his friend and co-worker, Mao Tse Zhou, U.S.-educated new generation politicians
- The old Navy Admiral, mentor to the new leaders

The Terrorists

Chinese:
- Major General Weng Tso Chang, Chinese NBC expert, fake UN diplomat, primary leader of the terrorist team
- Colonel Mou Shan Wu, Chinese NBC expert, fake UN diplomat

Arabs:
- Professor Adwar Al Naimi (Florida State University)
- Abdula Mattar, Jordanian terrorist & Chicago bomber
- Sofwan Koheggi, Kuwait Jordanian terrorist & NYC bomber
- Unnamed terrorists for LA bombing

Latinos:
- Carlos (Che) Barrientos, Ecuadorian Communist leader
- Paco Rodriguez, Mexican propane truck drive
- Emiliano Bazan and Jorge Estrella, Paco's cousins

Table of Contents

12

Chapter 1 – The American Analysis

10 August 2005 - Washington, D.C.

The new American president, Democrat John Warrington, and his vice president, Daniel McLaughlin, had barely squeaked through the 2004 election, winning by less than a mere 18,000 of the popular votes and by only 7 votes in the Electoral College.

The closeness of the race notwithstanding, John Warrington viewed himself as the voice for the poor, the oppressed, the mentally unstable, the unionized, the multi-culturalists, and the downtrodden: all those who, for some reason or other, had failed to make their mark or reach their goals in the most wonderful and prosperous nation in the world. The image Warrington conveyed to the American public and the media was of a glib, well-educated speaker, reasonably attractive and extremely wealthy. In reality, he was an arrogant, pompous, and self-serving politician who looked down on the so-called lower classes and undereducated as masses who had to be looked after by their better and wiser leaders.

Vice President Daniel McLaughlin was of a much different breed and philosophy, as he had been born into the masses of the undereducated and poor, which the president so disliked and only pandered to for votes.

The match-up of these two opposites was needed to secure the Electoral College votes of the Southern states for Warrington, given his unpopularity in the South and many parts of the Mid- and far-Western states. That they were able to pull it off at all was a miracle, based on most

15

Americans' penchant for placing job security, personal gain, and change simply for its own sake over national security, national safety, and international affairs... even over the various and numerous illegal immigration issues. The on-again/off-again terrorist threats seemed by now to bore average Americans, rather than to enlighten or concern them. The occasional alerts delighted the terrorists and eventually caused most Americans to lose sight of the enemy and the dangers awaiting them.

Today, August 10th, 2005, the President and his staff were assembled with the Joint Chiefs of Staff, the National Security Advisor, and representatives of the Centers for Disease Control and Prevention (CDCP), the Federal Emergency Management Agency (FEMA), and the Chief Officer of the U.S. Army Medical Research Institute of Infectious Diseases. They were gathered there to receive the latest briefings by the CIA and FBI on terrorist activities. The present speaker was Steven Pickings, the CIA liaison, who was informing them about message intercepts, movements of known key terrorist operatives, and the overall global view of the terrorists' activities recorded as of that morning.

The usual questioning by the same people who already knew the answers was in progress, as these springboards continued to re-verify what had previously been presented, enabling the questioners to be perceived as astute and interested. In actuality, all the participants were somewhat bored, as this presentation about the same high-threat level of terrorist transmissions was a repeat, with neither new input nor new revelations. Pickings sped up and ended his briefing with hardly a mutter from the assembled senior officials.

James K Matthews, FBI Special Agent to the White House, began his portion of the briefing next. "Mr. President, Mr. Vice President, distinguished ladies and gentlemen. Our Counter-Terrorist Intelligence Services have put together some very disturbing trends, and I will attempt to tie these together to provide a better picture of the direction these trends seem to be going. Some of what I say may sound like a rehash of past intelligence information that you have all read before, but when pieced together, it presents a much more ominous situation."

"As you all know, in 2002 Fidel Castro managed to assemble a coalition of government leaders and officials from Cuba, Brazil, Venezuela, Ecuador, Iran, and Red China. His goal was to support terrorist groups from different regions and ideological philosophies, but the same objective: to hasten the demise of the USA as the world's economic and business leader and the only remaining military superpower."

President Warrington was already in a bad mood, and he tore into Matthews by angrily asking, "Are you suggesting that my decision to pull out of Iraq is the real basis for the formation of this coalition?"

"No sir," replied Matthews, "This coalition was formed during the Bush Administration in June, 2002, and has been on-going since that time. I believe that the present chaos we see in Iraq under the UN's control would have occurred whether or not we had remained there."

Not to be outdone, Vice President McLaughlin chimed in. "In spite of what you right-wing fascists in the FBI might want to believe, I served my country in time of war, and I am a patriot. I don't want to hear any suggestions that the UN or our back-in-the-fold allies are a part of some giant conspiracy, so just watch what you say in this briefing, G- Man!"

Embarrassed and at a loss to understand the anger directed at him, Special Agent Matthews quickly debated in his mind whether to quit the FBI then and there and simply leave the briefing, or remain at his post and hang on for his full retirement a mere 15 months away. Holding back his anger - and recalling that the Vice President had been a Navy finance officer in Vietnam and was unlikely to have seen combat - Matthews slowly replied, "Sir, I was appointed to this position by former President Bill Clinton and was recommended for it by the head of the Senate Intelligence Committee, who was also, I might add, a Democrat. I also served several tours in combat as an Army Infantry Officer in Vietnam, and I am not a right-wing fascist. If you wish me to leave, I have a backup briefer available outside this room right now and he can take over from here if that is what you wish."

U.S. Army General Jonathan Paxton, Chairman of the Joint Chiefs, spoke up. "Gentlemen, this is a very important briefing, and I think we should all calm down and let Agent Matthews continue before this becomes some sort of pissing contest!"

The President said, "General Paxton, you're right. I got off to a bad start this morning with those damn Republicans calling for my head because of that damn train derailment in California. They seem to think it was a terrorist attack, and I have been unable to convince them otherwise. I told them we have enough right-wing militias up in Montana and Idaho to expect it to be their kind of work. I even agreed that it could also be some of the environmentalist nut cases, or, who knows, maybe even some disgruntled postal worker. But they seem convinced it's overseas terrorists, and so the headlines today will report that we've become soft on terrorists, even though we've only been in office eight months. Damn it, I don't need this now, I need to pass legislation to correct all the past administration's screw- ups and to get the Europeans working with us again. Agent Matthews, I apologize for my outburst, and I'll even apologize for Dan, as well. Please continue."

Calmed down by the President's remarks, Agent Matthews thought to himself, "Jesus H. Christ, and I voted for these morons! They remind me of that hate-filled Clinton Administration that seemed to despise everything military, everything to do with the Intelligence and Security Services, everything to do with government, and even with their own Secret Service Security details. How could I ever have convinced myself to support people like that again? Forgive me, GWB."

In the nanoseconds it took to go through this thought process, Agent Matthews decided to tell them the truth and the hell with his career. After all, the nation's safety might be at stake.

So, Matthews found his place and began again. "As I was saying, this coalition was formed with Latino leaders who were either communist sympathizers or outright card-carrying Communist leaders within their respective countries. What they did was to agree to discard the Communist labels and rhetoric and run for office as populist political leaders. With much assistance from Castro and his overseas backers, a lot of money was collected to support these new leaders in their quest for control of their respective nations and presidencies. Large payoffs to key industrialists, politicians, military leaders, and police officials allowed these selected, charismatic leaders to advance rapidly, and soon they were all in place, along with their key agents. We have a few moles in place, and others who have been religiously following the careers of these former Communists. Their rise to the top has been very rapid and quite successful, mainly due to political payoffs and then extreme control measures with opponents."

Matthews could not help but notice the smirks on the faces of the President and Vice President at the payoff remark. He continued, "We also know that representatives from the Lebanese Hezbolla, the Palestinian Hamas, the Iranian Intelligence Services, Saudi Arabia's Al Qaeda, Peru's Shinning Path, Colombia's FARC, Cuba's Intelligence Services, and most oddly, Red China's Intelligence Services, are also involved. They've met frequently over the past two years in all the Latin American countries named, but they do not seem to ever meet with the Latinos in either Iran or China. Considering that each major group of terrorists has its own leaders and obviously very different agendas, they seem on the surface to be odd bedfellows. But the one thread that seems to pull them all together is the desire to see our nation fall from its world leadership position, and to use chaos and havoc to accomplish these goals. We should expect attacks from any quarter, and we should also be prepared for the possibilities of WMD attacks across our nation. The Chinese seem to be...."

The President could no longer contain himself, and spoke. "Agent Matthews, that was a good briefing, and we appreciate your time. However, I want to add that your doomsday scenario is being addressed by both our State

Department and my own office. I spoke to the UN Secretary General this morning, who assured me of their complete cooperation in regards to our troop withdrawals from the South Korean peninsula, from the entire Middle East region except for our Naval flotillas, and from Afghanistan-which will fall under UN and NATO control, as well as partially our own as well. Military and police operations in South and Central America will cease, as will those in Africa, since we have no business in any of these nations' internal affairs."

One could have heard a pin drop, as the flabbergasted leaders tried to grasp the significance of it all. The "But, Buts" were cut short by the President's hand raised for quiet. "We have, or I should say, had a choice to continue the status quo, which will inevitably sooner or later lead to war. As your Commander-in Chief, I have chosen to avoid war with all nations and have been given assurances that those who might have intended to harm us will also pull back, and thus allow us to form a true and lasting peace for this world and to avoid the possibility of an Armageddon."

"Some of you may disagree with this one opportunity to save ourselves from a long, costly, and continuous war that will create countless casualties on all sides. If you cannot support my decision, then please leave your letter of resignation on the way out. But I hope you will agree not only to support my administration, but to be a part of bringing world peace to all the peoples of the world."

With that, the President left the room, Vice President in tow, to the astonishment of the gathering. Many in that room, particularly the military officers, thought long and hard about which choice they would make.

Chapter 2 – The Terrorist Analysis

13 August 2005

The Chinese

The two Red Army officers, under cover as UN diplomats on a convention and business tour, were hardly noticed as they arrived at the secret meeting location; they had their valid diplomatic passports anyway, as further protection from government authorities, if required.

They arrived there on August 13th, 2005, a day early for the planning meeting with their Latino and Arab counterparts in a large, older, rented home, which had been a former hunting lodge and long unused since the original owners had died years before. The former owners' offspring, having no use for hunting or the lodge, had then sold it to a wealthy Canadian-Chinese businessman. It was located far enough away from cities or towns that even prying eyes might not notice so diverse a collection of people.

The two officers had selected Canada for their first meeting due to its easy entry by foreigners, which had been true ever since the Canadian government changed to an open immigration policy that welcomed almost anyone, especially businessmen. The others would join them the next day, arriving from their various homelands and hideouts. The leaders of each cell would be separated from their comrades, who would be staying at an older, out-of-the-way motel several miles away.

Colonel Mou Shan Wu and Major General Weng Tso Chang were Nuclear, Biological, and Chemical experts. Wu was a physician specializing in nuclear medicines, who held a Masters Degree in Microbiology. General Chang was a scientist with PhDs in Physics, Engineering, and Math who had worked on the various types of rocketry and nuclear weaponry now stored in the Chinese military arsenals. They had both studied abroad in their youth, and each held Bachelor of Science degrees from France and Britain, as well as degrees in Political Science from a Chinese military university. Further, both had served as young men in the Chinese equivalent of the American Special Forces, had seen military action on the India border, the old Soviet border region, and had also served in several Latin American and African countries as advisors and observers. Colonel Wu had even served as a spy and a conduit for the exchange of terrorists, arms and information with the Chinese embassies in three Arab nations. Both officers had killed in combat operations, and both were well versed in several forms of the martial arts, although their ages and ailments now limited their ability to practice those arts with any proficiency. Now they relied on their staff of well-trained Chinese Special Forces members, assigned directly and solely to them from the Chinese Embassy in Canada.

The two officers had traveled for the past year across the U.S. posing as Chinese businessmen, or, as needed, as UN diplomats on fact-finding missions. They were thus able to garner a wide and diverse perspective on American culture, politics, government, industry, and most importantly, on U.S. military targets. They both spoke reasonably fluent, though accented, conversational English.

They traveled alone at times, or together when the opportunities arose, and especially where and when they thought they would not be noticed. They had formed opinions of Americans from the world of academia, the diplomatic arena, and through eating frequently at the lower-priced fast-food restaurants such as Denny's, McDonalds, Burger King, etc. They also dined at Italian, Chinese, and American restaurants and steak houses in order to understand the thinking and views of the so-called "average" American.

Their impressions were that the average American was poorly educated and prone to use clichés during conversations, which often evolved around such meaningless discussions as the recent activities of athletes, entertainers, neighbors, co-workers, or even their bosses. When government or politics were discussed, it was with a negative slant more often than not, as though all government officials and political leaders were either dumb or crooks, and as though they were all somehow being mistreated or cheated. The fact that they lived in the greatest nation ever known to mankind never seemed to enter their muddled thinking or their self-centered, selfish interests. The Chinese officers often shook their heads at the shallowness, unconcern, and outright stupidity of the "average American."

These impressions had been relayed to the Chinese Military High Command, which had concluded that today's Americans were not like those of old. The average American's patriotism, in the view of the Chinese High Command, was as fleeting as the latest hit song or sports score, and most would quickly seek a compromise or even a surrender to end any continued violence against their homeland. The High Command expected them to resist initially, but as more horrific events occurred, the Chinese expected that the nation's mood would change quickly to seek an end to all the bloodshed. In case the resistance massed in militarily tactical, targeted locations, the High Command's plan was to quickly destroy the few (albeit millions) who chose to fight, through the use of biological or chemical warfare or even nuclear weapons.

Americans who had once been strong and patriotically united, were now merely a disunited and disorganized bunch of greedy, self-centered individuals who could not think much beyond their personal needs and desires. Most had lost faith in their God, their government and themselves, with many relying on drugs and alcohol to mask their sorry lives by remaining in a state of almost perpetual semi-intoxication.

This was all very remarkable to the Chinese High Command, as America had provided the best living conditions known throughout the world. In the past, the Americans had been hardened warriors, inventors, and high achievers in all endeavors, from space and undersea exploration visionaries, to world leaders in medicine, agriculture, aviation, finance, automotives, sales, marketing, production, transportation, etc. At one time, they had even been the leaders in the coal and ore mining industries, along with textiles, shipbuilding, education, steel manufacturing, clothing, shipping, wood products, gas and oil production and refining, and so many other industries now defunct or mere shadows of their former selves. Most of the industry losses had resulted from union demands, along with environmental and related laws and regulations used to restrict or prohibit production and manufacturing, thus making these industries uncompetitive with overseas companies; and the American owners eventually simply closed their facilities.

The Chinese knew that Americans had once believed in hard work, in their God, and in the American Dream that had told them that opportunity existed in America for anyone to succeed, if they chose to do so. Even immigrants with little schooling or skilled trades had been able to succeed in this enlightened nation through learning and by working long hours. And even if these first generation immigrants were not themselves so successful, their children had every opportunity to become successful if they tried. America had fared quite splendidly after WWII and throughout most of the remainder of the 20th century, but that had all begun to change in the mid 1960s.

During that tumultuous decade, American socialists and Communists had successfully used the public education system to "dumb down" the nation in order to allow the world a better chance to compete with America. Much of the shift in education was brought about by the National education Association (NEA), a Union now of some 2.7 million members started in 1857 "to elevate the character and advance the interests of the profession of teaching and to promote the cause of popular education in the United States." Their smaller rival the American Federation of Teachers changed their course regarding their goals in 1997 with a new union president and today is almost indistinguishable from the NEA.

Not much criticism was addressed towards these unions prior to the 1960s, but with the promotion of school integration and the increasing costs demanded by these unions they became more transparent to the public. This in turn caused more interest in education and which was now being addressed by parents, who then began the questioning of these unions and the curriculums being taught in the nations High Schools. These unions continued to grow and expand and thus gained enormous political power, which allowed the unions to dictate and demand changes from their local and state governments.

With the election of a new AFL/CIO President, an avowed Marxist and an all-but-card-carrying communist, all American unions turned a hard left in their political direction and so the "dumbing down" of American high school students took off even more rapidly in directions never dreamed possible in the past. The leftist strategy had finally born the much of the desired fruit by the early 1980s, by which time American children from elementary through Secondary and High Schools, were expressing their displeasure with adults and all authority figures through the use of foul language, as well as disdain for authority figures, and even outright rebellion towards all adults in some instances.

Due to society's litigious nature by then, they had even learned to threaten teachers and school administrators with lawsuits for real or imagined offenses or slights. By 2004, American children ranked 41st in international scholastic achievement standings, and though many public high-school graduates were barely able to read or write beyond a sixth grade level, most somehow managed to complete high school. However, for many, their main achievement was simply to attend classes often enough to pass their courses, and then obtain that all-important high school diploma stating that they were now HS graduates.

The Chinese "diplomats" had learned in their travels around America that in the 1970s, school dress codes were changed to allow students the "freedom" to wear casual clothes to school–jeans, T-shirts, sneakers. Then, with the help of an accelerating number of ACLU lawsuits, ever more crude and demeaning slogans and images began appearing on T-shirts, which contributed to a further downgrading of school culture, while asserting their dubious First Amendment rights.

With more and more parents working outside the home–and an increasing number of single-parent homes– more and more children were being raised by daycare providers, with a corresponding decrease in oversight of what their kids were wearing, watching and listening to on TV, radio or on music recordings. The cultural influences of an increasingly left-leaning political influence coupled with an unwholesome Hollywood bent, it eventually began showing up in what the children were wearing, saying and doing. For instance, it never seemed to enter the minds of supposedly-educated instructors or concerned parents that allowing 13- and 14-year old girls to attend school dressed like young hookers or porn stars, might be detrimental to either their self-image or their learning abilities.

Meantime, their male counterparts were coming to school dressed like punk corner drug dealers and street hoodlums. This combination was most assuredly the perfect way to insure classroom disruptions and a lack of concentration on the subjects being taught. But many parents, afraid of upsetting their little darlings and overcome by guilt for not spending more time with them, ended up over-indulging their already self-indulgent offspring, and they allowed this appalling lack of dress standards and rude behavior to permeate the public schools and become the norm. Inevitably, this promoted the formations of gangs, clubs and an almost unanimous disdain for schoolwork as well as the proper testing of individual intellectual abilities. Those who showed promise were labeled "nerds" by their dumb and hoodlum-like counterparts.

These problems had been further exacerbated by the insistence of parents with children with state-diagnosed learning disabilities or physical deformities to have their children included in the regular classes, thus leading to even more classroom distractions and chaos. "Special Education" teachers were supposed to attend classes with each Special Ed child. But shortages of these teachers, plus the prohibitive costs of maintaining a one-to-one ratio, precluded this ideal concept from being implemented, and so regular teachers were often stuck trying to teach not only their often-unruly 'normal' students, but also the disruptive Special Ed students.

Many schools had found that sending the most unruly or uncaring students out to work part time, ostensibly to learn a trade, offered some respite from the class clowns and troublemakers. This at least allowed those students to obtain spending monies, while simultaneously obtaining school credit. The only problem was that they learned little, and many had trouble even counting change, much less learning a new trade. By the beginning of the 21st century, the public schools were nearly a lost cause, as the increased government funding and testing thrown at the problems failed to produce better educated students across the nation.

Meanwhile, college and university professors and instructors, particularly those teaching the Liberal Arts (history, sociology, philosophy, psychology, etc.), were teaching non-traditional alternatives to the American free market system and the nation's democratic ideals. Instead, they promoted the philosophies of socialism, communism, anti-Americanism, and outright anarchy along with the so-called "benefits" of multiculturalism, including the concepts of a "one-world" government model. The eager-to-please and easy-to-manipulate young minds ("young skulls filled with mush," as one famous conservative talk radio host called them) lapped up these ideals of thwarting authority, and with finding fault with all of the present governmental systems in the U.S. College students were thus systematically seduced into supporting extremist causes and values, and also into believing in an ideal world of relative values (whatever makes sense to you is right).

As these undereducated students graduated into the real working world, many turned to drugs and alcohol (or continued the use begun in high school and college) to avoid fighting the bureaucracy at their workplace, or of accepting the responsibilities of either wealth building or parenting. Many Americans in their 30s and 40s were no more aware of world or national problems and situations now than they were when they left high school, and even after college or university graduation. This mass of theoretically educated people could be expected, in times of crisis, to blame everyone and everything else, but never themselves.

So the Chinese High Command viewed the new average Americans as bloated, greedy and self-serving slobs, who would no more risk their lives defending their own nation than they would serve in their military when they had the opportunity to do so. The American people and nation thus appeared ripe for attack and subjugation.

The Arabs

The Arabs viewed the Americans as a decadent and evil people deserving of the wrath of Allah, not only because they had sponsored and supported the Arabs' hated enemy-Israel, but also because they also believed the Americans had stolen the gas and oil products of the Middle East in order to build up their own nations. Justified or not, this left the Arab peoples wallowing in anger and many with a hatred of all things Western.

Millions of Arabs who remained poor and hungry, and in need of decent housing and medical treatments, had been humiliated far too often by both the Israelis and the evil Americans. To them, it was obviously the fault of the West that their own leaders had failed to educate their people, that is, much beyond the readings of the Koran and basic reading and writing skills.

Arabs were extremely reluctant to accept responsibility for either their own ineptness or their laziness: their desire was non-existent to learn or work hard at the unskilled jobs that many were best suited for because of their poor educations. Because they refused to blame their tribal or national leaders for either their present societal conditions or their poverty, they were susceptible to allowing religious leaders to direct their anger at the Western powers with all their wealth and lack of "true" religious beliefs. To them, the West's failure to accept the true Prophet as its religious leader was not only blasphemous, but also an affront to the enlightened Arab world, and the justifiable penalty for that behavior was "death to all infidels."

No, the Americans, Europeans, and Israelis all deserved what was coming, and they, the Arab world, would be proud to lead the vanguard of this tidal wave of Islamic terror onto the homeland of the hated larger enemy. If they themselves died while helping to destroy their main enemy, the Americans, then that was Allah's will and was meant to be. If not, then Allah had granted them another opportunity to strike down infidels with yet another blow. Being fatalists in general, the Arabs sought no middle ground or compromise, and they would give no quarter to, nor expect it from the infidels. This was a religious war to them, a jihad; as far as they were concerned, all Westerners and infidels of other nations could die. Muslims would someday rule again, and either all the world would bow to the Arabs and their true religion, or they would pay the consequences for their failure to accept or respect the men of the true faith.

The Chinese officers viewed the Arab terrorists they had met as zealots and religious fanatics of the worst kind. But for now, they could prove useful in the overall plans for the defeat of the mighty United States of America.

The Latinos

The Latino terrorists had a different belief system: they had long ago discarded their religious upbringings and backgrounds in favor of Communism or socialism in some form or other. However, they still retained a vestigial belief in the Almighty and an afterlife. Their religious beliefs had always been weak, and the inability of the priests to answer their faith-based questions had left them as skeptics. However, their overall philosophy was to change the world for a more equitable redistribution of goods and services, rather than for the complete destruction of mankind or some other form of Armageddon, as envisioned by their Arab terrorist counterparts. So while the Latinos stood more for changing the world than for its destruction, they also realized that their own lives could be forfeit in this combined effort to bring down the world's richest and only superpower. In their reasoning, the U.S. had long stood in the way of the future development of all mankind, and now it had to be brought down.

Many Latinos believed that the Americans had stolen Mexican territories and humbled and humiliated the Latino people of the world, both by interfering in the affairs of their sovereign nations and by the disrespect shown the campensinos or workers, who had migrated to the U.S. over the past hundreds of years. While their anger and wrath were directed primarily at white Americans, their overall world goals appeared somewhat limited to the Chinese, as they were not quite able to conceive of a world controlled by Latinos. Instead, they saw one in which they could participate as equals in some vague form of a world government, under a communist or socialist form of government. With such limited goals and objectives and only a cloudy concept of how they could force the world to become equal and united, the Latino terrorists would be the easiest to manipulate and control, at least in the opinion of the Red Chinese officers.

Chapter 3 – The Terrorists Meet

14 August 2005

The terrorist group leaders were now all at the former hunting lodge, whose out-of-the-way location in Western Canada provided the perfect setting for meeting and planning the upcoming "WMD attacks on America!"

As the individual cell members had arrived the night before, each member of the Latino and Arab groups was driven by Chinese Security force members to rooms at an old motel site, about seven miles away. This would allow the members to be quickly and easily briefed by their leaders before returning home, and then back to their planned US attack locations. They had been instructed to remain indoors where food and drink, TV and radio were provided, while their leaders were meeting. Furthermore, they were instructed not to communicate with the other groups or cell members, lest they give away important names or information. While this was an obviously sensible security measure for this most important mission, this setting seemed strange to many, since the outer security guards were well-armed Asians who appeared to control the secret meeting locations, the planning agendas, the transportation, and all security and lodging needs.

The Chinese senior officers were well aware that there might be some dissent from the Arab or Latino leaders. They were prepared to deal with any eventuality, since all the guards within the lodge and around its perimeter were Chinese Special Forces members and under the direct control of General Chang and Colonel Wu.

The meeting began with all the leaders seated around a large rectangular table, with the Arab and Latino members seated on opposite sides. Colonel Wu was at the head of the table with General Chang opposite him, so they could both better observe the proceedings and view the expressions of each individual. The five Chinese Special Forces soldiers inside the lodge remained standing against the walls, and while armed, appeared casual in the holding of their rifles, a strategy they had rehearsed in order to avoid alarming the cell leaders and to present an appearance of non concern with the actual proceedings.

Colonel Wu began the meeting by asking the soldiers to bring tea for the two Chinese officials, Arabic coffee for that group, and Colombian coffee for the Latinos. He then welcomed everyone and asked if anyone needed anything more or else to use the bathroom now, in order to avoid disrupting the meeting later on. Many took to the toilets, while the others remained chatting about their upcoming opportunity to defeat America with their long planned and dreamed of attacks.

When everyone was seated, Colonel Wu stood and reminded them that the Arab terrorist group seniors had approved the operations, as had the leaders of the various Arab nations, who were both aware of and supported the attack plans. Furthermore, the leaders of Cuba, Venezuela, Brazil, and Ecuador had also agreed to the plan, in case the Latino cell leaders had any reservations. Furthermore, he reminded them, it had been agreed during the secret Sao Paulo meetings in Brazil that the Chinese would control and manage all attack operations, as they were the only nuclear nation involved which also maintained a gigantic standing military force.

The impetuous and self-righteous Professor Adwar Al Naimi (of Florida State University notoriety) jumped up and stated heatedly, "We know what our missions and assignments are regarding this event, but we have not been briefed on the follow-on stages. I demand that we all know what is planned in the future, and we intend to be involved in that planning as well, as we were never asked to be involved in the initial planning phases for these attacks and do not intend to be directed to our mission goals by outsiders, God willing." All the Arab members nodded in agreement.

Colonel Wu replied, "Professor Al Naimi, please understand that these issues were addressed with your leaders, who have approved allowing the Chinese military to plan, support, coordinate, and command all aspects of these scheduled operations. General Chang and I, along with our security elements are here for that express purpose. If you object to the process or the control elements, then you must contact your superiors. But know now that they will repeat what I have just stated. Now please, allow me to continue with the meeting." The professor sat down, but his face had turned a darker shade of red from his anger and embarrassment at being considered nothing more than a mere underling, that was, to the ungodly and atheistic Chinese Communists.

Colonel Wu resumed, explaining that they had to check and recheck every piece of equipment and every planned movement, including the timing of each practice run to insure they would remain hidden once they were on US soil. The Americans were already alerted, or soon would be, so if they all followed the plan there would be no excuse for failing either to accomplish their assigned missions or to return to their pre-planned safe havens. He then told them, "You, the leaders, will alone bear complete responsibility for any errors or omissions, or for the lose any of your cell members."

At this stage of the one-way discussion, the professor's face had turned an even darker shade of red, and he could not help himself any longer. When Wu went back to an easel to retrieve a diagram, the professor leaned over towards his fellow Arabs and whispered, "These yellow dog infidels are not going to be in charge for long, just wait and see, we will change their plans along the way to suit our own purposes." Not knowing the backgrounds of either Colonel Wu and General Chang or any of the Chinese Special Forces Officers, the Arabs were unaware that their whispered conversation was being copied via listening devices, although everyone at the table overheard it.

While none of the Latino terrorists spoke a word of Arabic or Chinese, two of the Chinese Special Forces officers spoke fluent Spanish. But what Al Naimi did not know was that four of the Chinese—the two Chinese Special Forces guards who also spoke Spanish and the two senior officers—also spoke fluent Arabic and understood the entire whispered conversation. Also unknown to the Arabs and Latinos, the devices in General Chang's ears, which appeared to be hearing aids, were actually high-level receivers that picked up all nearby sounds and conversations including those from the toilet area.

As Wu returned to the table with his diagram, he noted out of the corner of his eye that General Chang had just nodded his head ever so slightly, while looking straight at the professor. The nearby Special Forces officer fired twice with his silenced pistol into the head of the college professor, who slumped forward with his eyes rolling to the top of his head, a sure sign he was dead. Everyone immediately pushed away from the table, not knowing what to expect next and realizing that they were unarmed and at the mercy of the Chinese officers.

Another nod from General Chang prompted several other guards to take the professor's body outside. A quiet unease was showing on the faces of the terrorist cell and group leaders as they registered that one of their own had just been shot by the Chinese soldiers, removed from the building like a dead animal, and that he had been a Terrorists leader and a college professor!

Once the body was removed, Colonel Wu began speaking again, but a raised hand from the Ecuadorian, Carlos (Che) Barrientos, stopped the Colonel in mid-sentence. "Yes, Mr. Barrientos?" he asked. Carlos Barrientos, stood and asked, "May I ask a question without offending anyone?" Wu was visibly annoyed, but replied, "Please ask your question now so that we can proceed."

Barrientos said, "Well, I came here with the impression or understanding that we were all in this together, and therefore were viewed as equals on this mission, but that apparently is not the case, so could you please explain our part in this mission?"

Wu nodded for Barrientos to be seated and then replied. "Mr. Barrientos, as I stated earlier, your governments or organizations have approved our running this mission and retaining control of all personnel, equipment, and movements. Your job, and that of all others here, is simply to follow our orders and directives and not to question our authority or our plans for your groups or cells. Is that clear enough?" Barrientos, still trying to get the last word in, said, "With all due respect, that was not my agreement with my leaders, and had I known this to be the case, I would not have volunteered my group for this mission."

A nod and eye movement from General Chang caused two of the Chinese guards to move quickly to Barrientos' side. The one on the right delivered a quick kidney blow to Carlos, and the other caught him before he fell to the floor. Carlos was in pain and gasping for breath as the guards lifted him off his feet and took him outside of the building.

Colonel Wu, now visibly annoyed, said again, "any more questions before we proceed?" The men at the table simply looked down, afraid to utter a sound. Wu said, "Here is the plan for each group or cell, and you are now to study it. If there are any questions concerning what your specific group or cell is to do or how to proceed, simply raise your hand and we will discuss the issue or matter in that small area over by the bathroom. This is to ensure privacy and avoid interfering with the others studying their assignments. Furthermore, this prevents anyone from finding out any other groups or cell's targets, locations, or members. Is everyone clear on that?" All replied in unison, "Yes sir."

The group and cell leaders reviewed the specifics of their assignments and had numerous questions regarding timing, schedules, equipment, communications, safe houses, return routes to safety, and needed supplies. These were individually discussed and agreed upon as being both practical and sensible for their specific mission. The meeting took over seven hours, but all were confident now that they could fulfill their assigned tasks. They also understood that the timing of the events was crucial to the overall plan and subsequent goals. As they departed the buildings for the mini-buses, they all saw Carlos Barrientos digging a rather large grave, with Professor Al-Naimi's body laid out beside the gravesite. They all knew they would never see either the Professor or Carlos again and smiled to themselves, realizing how wise they had been to keep quiet and not challenge the Chinese officers. Some were thinking that the Chinese might some day pay for this, but then quickly changed their thoughts to other things, lest there become a need for a third grave.

The planning process was completed, the terrorists were briefed, and now the only major items of concern for the Chinese were to ensure the weapons, pesticide trucks, and biological and chemical agents were in place and that all the required equipment was in good working order. Soon the Americans would encounter the enormity of the attacks and would quiver like frightened dogs, knowing that further attacks were being prepared for use against them.

Chapter 4 - The President's First War Room Meeting

21 August 2005 - Washington, D.C.

Less than two weeks after their last meeting, the Americans met again in the President's war room, but with only a subset of the individuals who had been present earlier, but including the Vice President, Daniel McLaughlin; Ed Pickings, the CIA Liaison Officer; James K. Matthews, the FBI's White House Special agent; and General Jonathon Paxton, Chairman of the Joint Chiefs of Staff. The talk was restrained, almost whispered, because the latest intelligence being sent to all agencies and the President's staff was both ominous and quite scary. The probability of a WMD event occurring in the U.S. had changed from possible to probable, and now to imminent. The latest efforts by the new president to work with allies like France, Germany, Red China, Italy, Spain, Japan, and all the Muslim nations, had produced many of the same old vows of support, but no new intelligence of value, or even any new or notable efforts to capture or question known terrorists residing in those nations.

The President's pleas to the UN members to allow the U.S. to work with them under his new non-interference polices had fallen on deaf ears: those nations had no wish to help the U.S. avoid being punished for its past real or perceived abuses, at least not by the UN delegate majority.

President Warrington was now nearing his wits' end, as he had agreed to everything that he thought the other nations wanted from the U.S.: from trade barrier reductions to more nations added to the preferred nations trading lists, and even to the extent of sharing the latest in secret weapons and computer technology with Red China, France, Russia, and of course, Britain. He had even hinted that the U.S. was amenable to the Kyoto Protocols, Special Weapons reductions, and even to becoming more "European" – or more socialistic – in its policies. But he had also had to tell them that it would take time to persuade the American people to these new ways.

This President had been fascinated by French intellectuals from an early age, just as had an actress-turned anti-war activist during an earlier period of U.S. history, besides he spoke the French language reasonably well. He also strangely reasoned that he truly knew and understood Europeans and the poor of the world including poor Americans. This belief was based on his associations with the upper classes of European societies at various periods in his life, and from talking to his parents' drivers or maids, whom he believed, provided the true views of the poor. His elite education at a top-level university, coupled with his extensive–primarily European–travels and the high-level briefings he had received as a member of the U.S. Congress, caused him to believe that he was not only prepared for the presidency, but rightfully deserved it. He had been rather taken aback by his very close win, as he had stated his views and plans more than adequately to the American public. If some had disagreed with his views, well then he expected they would soon see the righteousness of his cause, and the peace that would surely someday come to the nations of the world as a result of them.

But right now, he was both confused and more than a little upset that things were not going as he had planned, and, worse, that the nation was now under threat of WMD attacks on American soil. While he pondered how things could have gone so wrong so fast, he also had a horrible feeling that his political opponents had been right all along, and that his own beliefs may have been both idealistic and based on complete falsehoods. But it was far too late to back off now: the die was cast, and he had to live with the hand he'd been dealt. He was now afraid of his own judgment for the first time in his entire life, and it was almost as though he was becoming unglued.

This meeting began with Vice President Daniel McLaughlin attempting to take charge, since the president seemed to be in a pensive state of mind and was hardly paying attention to anything or anyone around him. McLaughlin could sense the fear and somber mood of the people gathered around the very large table in the war room. He began by reminding everyone of the major errors committed by the Intelligence agencies during the second Bush Administration's Gulf War, including the reports of that period predicting the presence of numerous WMDs, which had turned out not to be true; nor had the supposed friendly uprising to support the coalition forces occurred. He also reminded them that intelligence estimates and conclusions were often based on questionable or faulty intelligence, so they had to view the latest reports with some skepticism and not get all stirred up or down over the latest reports.

McLaughlin continued, telling the group, "We have received reports from numerous agencies and sources that indicate an attack on American soil is imminent. We're being told that many of the UN and Embassy diplomatic families are traveling overseas in unprecedented numbers, including the immediate families of the French, Italian, Belgian and German Ambassadors."

Before going on, he hastened to say that those last four nations were not confirmed as part of the so-called terrorist alliance. He went on. "Furthermore, most of these, and even many lower level officials, are themselves now going on leave or vacation outside of the U.S. The reports we're getting now also indicate that numerous spies, and even questionable allied nations like Canada and Mexico, have authorized their intelligence officials to pass the word on to our government that attacks are on the way. Their expectation is that thousands, if not hundreds of thousands of our citizens could die in the first hours or days of these planned attacks."

He forged ahead. "Other reports say that preparations are underway for subsequent attacks in order to defeat us completely and effectively. Finally, since the attackers are thought to be terrorists from many different groups and nations, and there is no single nation or individual with whom we can either negotiate or communicate. Because of these factors, the President has found himself isolated and unsupported by our former allies. In fact, from what we have gleaned through our intelligence sources, the terrorists themselves appear to have originated from various Muslim nations and South Americans countries, and we suspect they have some Communist Chinese and Iranian support, although those reports are not yet confirmed."

McLaughlin ended his review with a crooked smile, commenting, "While the U.S. can expect to receive some minor attacks, you need to understand that America isn't under some world conspiracy or gigantic global threat. Rather, it's only a test to shake up the will of the people and this administration."

When McLaughlin has finished speaking, Ed Pickings, the CIA Liaison Officer, stood up to begin the formal Presidential briefing with a repeat of much of what had been stated in the recent reports. He knew he didn't want to retire at this critical juncture, but he couldn't allow the Vice President's remarks of belittling his agency and the work and efforts of so many others to go unchallenged. He turned away from his audience and winked at the next briefer, James K. Matthews, FBI Special agent to the White House, and mouthed the words "been good to know you." Pickings turned and faced the assembled audience. His next comments startled everyone, who sat up straight and listened to his every word.

"Mr. Vice President, you have belittled and maligned all Intelligence operatives both good and bad, as well as the many who recently gave their lives, attempting to gather and provide the intelligence you so rudely and capriciously dismissed as possibly being in error. I can assure everyone at this meeting that the information is good. It's even been coming in from our own operatives and allies in countries like Syria and Iran, Venezuela, Brazil, and Ecuador. That's because the operatives fear we will nuke them as well, once the terrorists' ties to their leaders or intelligence services are established.

They expect those nations' leaders to say is that although they may have assisted the terrorists in the past, they are not responsible for any actions now taken by the terrorists against the U.S. and its people. In short, they will be trying to weasel out of any responsibility, yet it should be obvious to all that they played a very big part in supporting and supplying the terrorists, and they are most assuredly responsible for any coming WMD events to our nation."

"Additionally, the Iranians have deployed two of their three Diesel attack submarines through the Suez Canal and into the French port of Marseilles; their purported destinations include a later visit of one submarine scheduled to visit the port in Amsterdam, although no preparations appear to be underway as yet. The other sub is scheduled to leave tomorrow for Port Charles Marina at Bridgetown, Speight town in Barbados, a seaport presently run by the Red Chinese through the Hutchison Whampoa group. This port is only a short distance from the entrance to the Caribbean Sea, the Gulf of Mexico, and the Atlantic Ocean, and just a very short distance to the western side of the Panama Canal. Which, I might add, is also run and controlled by the Chinese Hutchison Whampoa group. What this means is that if they wish to attack our carrier fleets in the Mediterranean or closer to home, they will possess that ability."

"The third Iranian sub remains in Iranian waters, but as reported by numerous sources, which is in the briefing paper in front of you, it has been practicing sub attacks on passing cargo ships in the Straits of Hormuz. What this can mean is a suicidal attack on our fleet located within the confines of the Arabian, or as it's often called, the Persian Gulf."

"Therefore, each of these three submarines is or will be in place to cause harm to our naval fleets. While our Naval Forces and those of our coalition partners have been placed on alert, they can do nothing until an offensive strike has begun, and that could prove costly in terms of men, equipment, and future capabilities. Next..."

Vice President McLaughlin, angered by Pickings' earlier rebuff, stood up shouting, "Are you trying to tell us that the French, the Iraqis, the Chinese, and several of our Latin neighbors are in collusion to attack the United States? That is preposterous, and you had better have your information correct, or you will be briefing in Juno, Alaska, if you have a job at all."

At that point, a very tired looking President Warrington spoke out, "Oh, shut up, Daniel, and listen to what is being said." The startled Vice President, noting the smirks on many faces, was angered and embarrassed but sat down without a further murmur.

Agent Pickings continued, "As I was saying, the next concern is the deployment of nearly half of the Red Chinese fleet of 47 submarines into the Pacific region, with four subs deployed around Japan and four now deployed around the island of Taiwan. An additional seven have been tracked to the French Island groups of Isles Marquises and the Tuamoto Islands; these are simply skirting the various island groups. These Chinese subs appear to be located in a good position to intercept our Naval Forces that might be heading from Hawaii to the Far East. Two more of their subs were located near the Aleutian Islands, but they have gone into hiding. We expect to have their exact locations determined momentarily."

"Another Chinese sub pulled into port in Guayaqill, Ecuador, apparently for repairs to some malfunctioning or broken hydraulic pumps, but the port couldn't handle the sub's size, so it limped back to the Ecuadorian Galapagos

Islands to rendezvous with a sister sub. An Ecuadorian Navy war ship and a civilian barge have arrived there to assist with the needed repairs. Three more are on a port call near the city of Caracas, Venezuela, and their future destination is unknown at this time. However, we know that they passed through the Panama Canal two days ago."

"Likewise, two more Chinese subs are in the Cuban port of Havana and have been there for over a week. Their destination is also unknown at this time. The map here on the overhead projector shows the locations of all the subs: the Chinese are shown in red and the Iranian subs are shown in green. The Chinese Armed Forces are on alert, as are those of Iran, Cuba, Venezuela, Brazil, and Ecuador. Other nations of the Middle East have upgraded their alert status from normal to elevated, but not yet to full alert.

While the Russians have been providing us with intelligence updates and information regarding intercepts and agent reports, the French and Germans have been providing intelligence at a very slow rate and usually with qualifiers like "not verified," or "not reliable." So far, the British and Australians are the only ones stalking these subs, along with our own Navy, and they are providing reliable and up to date information."

"It appears that the attacks to our homeland are imminent, and the only allies we can really count on are the Brits and the Aussies. Our analysis suggests that during the first terrorist attacks, the subs will remain in place to determine the damage caused and our reactions to the attacks. If our nation will appears to be cracking or ready to surrender to the will of the terrorists, then the Chinese military will probably launch air and missile strikes and send their subs against our fleet, as they must insure our total defeat and also that we're willing to be subjugated. Otherwise, they would have to accept a partial defeat and share the spoils with the terrorists."

"It appears we have two choices: we accept defeat by either the terrorists or the Chinese military, or we must fight and strike first. We recommend striking first to lessen the damage and casualties to our own nation and forces, before they can strike us with a devastating, and possibly an unrecoverable, blow."

The faces around the large table were pale and wan, showing even greater worry than when the meeting began. All fell silent, except for General Paxton, Chairman of the Joint Chiefs. He arose and firmly stated, "Our forces have all been placed on Red Alert, our military's highest alert priority, and we all stand ready to follow your orders Mr. President."

Chapter 5 – The Terrorists Prepare

The end of August, 2005

By late August 2005, the Red Chinese, along with the Arab and Latino terrorists, had scouted their targeted areas just often enough to get the updates on any observable changes. They did their best to appear to be workers passing through or individuals with little interest in the specific locations. The initial targeted cities were all in the Southwest and South: San Diego, California, Houston, Texas, and Jacksonville, Florida. These states would be attacked by the Latino terrorists, who had easier and better access to the states bordering Mexico and with Florida nearest to the many nearby Caribbean Islands.

However, the terrorists attacking Florida planned to infiltrate through the Texas borders, as they were more likely to be picked up as illegal immigrants if they entered from the Island nations. The vials of biological agents had been smuggled into the U.S. for over a year before the planned attacks, providing ample time for the biological agents to be grown in small special laboratories. These small laboratories operated in the targeted cities, enabling easier transfer of the biological agents to the terrorists who would then release the agents. Because chemicals and containers for authorized pesticides were rarely checked by the local authorities, there was little chance of them being detected.

To inspect these chemicals properly, state or city inspectors would have had to don protective suits and then shower off when the inspections were completed, which all took too much time, effort, and work. Therefore, most of the inspections consisted of mere visual observations, the filling out the required forms, and occasionally cautioning against any observed discrepancies such as lose lids or leaks.

The toxic chemical gases and their containers had been transferred from Mexico over the U.S. borders under the guise of pesticide shipments from Mexican companies, with only one container per truckload containing the extremely poisonous and toxic gas agents. Thus, the chances were remote of that one container being found among hundreds of other verifiable pesticide containers. Nearly all the planned containers arrived in the U.S. cities without incident and once inside the U.S. border, the toxic gas containers could be easily transported by unknowing drivers to the targeted cities.

During this first phase of the initially planned attacks, the Chinese, Iranians, and supporting Latin American Embassies would be tasked with reporting the American response to the attacks, as well as where and how the Special WMD Hazard Teams would be deployed. Further, they were supposed to determine where and how the limited available medications and the national resources would be distributed to each city location."

The terrorists hoped that the vast majority of the WMD Hazmat Teams, equipment, and medications would be sent to these first three targeted locations, which would then conform nicely to the original Chinese plan: that is, before the initiation of the next attack phases. Thus, they anticipated a lapse of a week or more before the data from the first attacks could be processed and the analysis concluded, and then the adjustments made for the needed quantities and types of weaponry required for the subsequent attacks.

The plan for the first phase was to attack the three southern cities on September 11th, 2005, with both chemical and biological agents. In the case of the biological agents, they would be placed in the air conditioning ductwork systems in all major hospitals, as well as most fire department and police stations locations as possible. The reasoning was that, by incapacitating many of the key first responders, the chaos following the attack would prove even more devastating than it would have been otherwise. This was because many of the key elements of the WMD response plans would be eliminated or incapacitated. The first attacks would comprise a mixture of anthrax, bubonic plague and small pox agents in separate containers, and released at the same or nearly the same times in order to confuse the initial medical diagnosis, and prevent the use of the correct medication or responses.

The original concept for the use of chemical agents was to use American commercial pesticide trucks an release these toxic gases at night, in order to prevent the sunlight from dissipating the toxicity of the agents and to avoid detection. The pesticide trucks were to be loaded with the chemical agents, and then placed in a high elevation, preferably on a hill or mountain crest, where the prevailing winds would take the toxic agents towards the city centers. The trucks' pumps and motors would simply be turned on and left to run, and the terrorists who would take precautions and have antidote medications for themselves, would simply walk to a waiting vehicles and disappear away from the deadly gases and head towards their remote safe havens. The winds and motors would do all the work for them, and thus this was the easiest of all assignments.

However, as the Chinese Red Army officers thought more about this method of attack, the more they concluded that the casualty counts would be significantly limited by attacking at night, instead of during the day. They reasoned that most people would be at home at night, which would afford them with some basic protection from the release of the agents, as much would cling to the outer building frames and surfaces, and could then be washed down with solvents during daylight hours to render them harmless.

So, they changed the attack plan from night to daylight attacks, believing that many more people would be caught out in the open. Their new thinking was that although this might be riskier and less stealthy, it was more likely to provide a much higher contamination ratio and fear factor, which, after all, was their objective. They proposed the change to the timing of the initial attacks to the other terrorist leaders, who agreed to it just before they all left for their respective destinations.

The plan also included setting diversionary fires along the outskirts of all three target cities in order to divert the first responders–Police, Fire, and EMS personnel–from being available in large numbers at the onset of the WMD attacks, and when the biological and chemical agents would be released. The hills around San Diego and Houston were usually dry all year round, and fires, once ignited, would quickly spread. Jacksonville, Florida, was not quite as susceptible to large fires, primarily due to the numerous nearby rivers and streams and the lack of hills or high ground at that location. But patches of forests remained scattered about the city, and the numerous bridges were many and easy to block with pre-planned accidents.

Another tactic they planned to use was to pay Mexican drivers more than six months' pay to cause accidents on bridges or major highways, to divert attention to the accidents and fires and thus further enabling covert placement of the biological agents and chemical trucks at their intended locations. In the Chinese officers' eyes, little was being left to chance. But all those who were being used and who had remained outside of the terrorist's structure, were poor people being given considerable monies to perform their newly assigned tasks. Practically all of these newly hired individuals believed that their new benefactors were either drug dealers or perhaps insurance scam artists, but none was ever aware they were being used and paid for by foreign terrorists.

Suggestions to the drivers involved such ideas as having a friend drop some oil or other liquid ahead of their trucks or semi trucks, or appear to have been cut off, which provided the excuses for the planned accidents and therefore make the bribes seem even more acceptable. What poorly-paid truck Mexican driver could turn down a chance to make a half a year's pay for creating a minor accident that might tie- up some bridge or highway? Only two drivers refused the offers, fearing their bosses would fire them on the spot since their trucks were new and accident free.

Paco Rodriguez was one of the drivers, and he was a man who had worked hard all his life and loved his Cerveza or beer much as other working men. He usually drank with his distantly related cousins, Emiliano Bazan and Jorge Estrella, but they both always seemed to be short of money. Some days, they simply couldn't afford their favorite pastime of watching and flirting with the bar maids, drinking beer and telling stories of their upcoming wealth... wealth to be had through great dreams that never seemed to go as planned under the cloud of beer-sodden brains. Paco had a good reliable job that paid an acceptable wage, but little was left over after paying for his family's needs and his understood generous beer allowance. But Paco remained reasonably content, as he unlike many others, actually had a job. He seldom asked what his younger cousins were up to, suspecting it was probably illegal since they had both been in jail for petty theft and claimed that prevented them from getting a decent paying job. In short, like so many in Mexico with limited educations and few real skills, they had turned to petty theft as an occasional form of livelihood.

When Paco began showing up with larger amounts of money than normal for beer, which was additional money gained from taking propane cylinders to the U.S., Emiliano and Jorge figured that Paco had somehow got into the drug trade and they intended to join the party if they could. They knew Paco took his ten-year old, beat up Ford truck to the U.S. several times a week to collect propane cylinders from the nearby factory just south of Tijuana, Mexico, thanks to the NAFTA agreement. They also knew that Paco sometimes loaded the truck the day before, and then parked it at a friend's garage so that he could get an early morning start the next day. They found out that Paco's next run was on September 3rd and agreed that the drugs must be inside the cylinders, and so they decided to appropriate one cylinder and show Paco that they were onto his game and then cash in on the deal.

Thus, on the evening of August 31st, 2005, three days before Paco was scheduled to make his next run to the U.S., the cousins failed to show up at the bar; instead, they waited nearby until they saw Paco leave for home and then snuck into the garage where his truck was parked. Once inside and viewing the stacked up propane cylinders, they realized that all of them couldn't contain drugs. The Border Patrol would have checked at least some of them by now, and Paco would have been caught. So, they looked at each propane cylinder and noticed they all looked the same except for one near the center. This specific cylinder was older like the rest, but the lettering and numbering seemed recent, unlike the others whose lettering seemed worn through frequent use.

So, Emiliano and Jorge took the one differently labeled cylinder off the truck, and took it over to the storage compartment of the garage where they had seen some welding tools and torches. They were smart enough to empty the propane cylinder, that is, after many attempts with various tools. Once the cylinder was emptied, they decided to cut into it to see if there was a false compartment on the bottom where they suspected the drugs were stored.

While neither man knew how to weld properly, they had watched others and felt they could do the job, even if it wouldn't be neat the way real welders could cut and weld. After numerous attempts, they finally managed to burn a few holes into the bottom portion, releasing a liquid onto the floor. They couldn't tell what it was from its color, so they attempted to find out by tasting it.

Disgusted at not finding the drugs, they left everything there and went to the cantina for a few beers before it closed, all the while lamenting on how yet another good plan had gone awry.

By the second day after they had tasted and splattered the ingredients of the cylinder on themselves while welding through the bottom of the cylinder, the two men became very sick, and after much discussion finally checked themselves into the local free clinic. The doctors were unsure about what was causing their ailments and demanded to know what they had done before the onset of their illness. Hesitantly, they realized they were getting much worse as large pus sores began popping up all over their upper bodies. Soon they got very scared and confessed, telling the clinic doctors all they had done and where the cylinder was located.

Paco was enraged when he found the damaged cylinder near his truck, now empty and torched over many sections and with something leaking out the bottom. But he made his scheduled run to the U.S. as usual on September 3rd, planning to tell his contactor that he was short one cylinder because it had been damaged during loading, and there had been no one was around to replace it. Paco hoped this would get him off the hook if anyone questioned his short load, as accidents do happen. While he suspected that drugs of some type were probably fitted into the containers, he had asked no questions and wanted no answers, nor even why he was paid so much for his now regular runs to San Diego.

He got home that evening feeling a bit ill, but got his second wind and returned to the bar that evening to await his cousins. He had a couple of beers and then started sweating profusely, and before long, he was throwing up. He went to the same free clinic as his cousins and was surprised to find them there along with other family members. He then began to feel very frightened at that point.

The next day, the clinic called the U.S. Centers for Disease Control and Prevention and the Homeland Security Department for help. For the first time in 35 years, Americans were allowed on Mexican soil armed with weapons and with HAZMAT teams, who attempted to stem the spread of the smallpox now running rampant in that Mexican border town.

People in Paco's town became scared and many panicked, and by September 6th, a large number had run to families located far in the interior of Mexico. Thus began the further spread of the smallpox agent, long before its intended and scheduled use.

Chapter 6 – A Congressman Holds a Secret Meeting

8 September 2005 - Washington, D. C.

Due to the ominous reports of an impending attack on the U.S. by unknown terrorists, Representative Barney Albertson (D-Kansas), Speaker of the House of Representatives and a member of its Intelligence Committee, convened a meeting on 8 September 2005 with Senator Susan Pelerine (D-Texas), the Senate Majority Leader and President Pro Tempore[1], along with other senior members of the Senate's Intelligence Committee and key Agency personnel.

The latter attendees included: Alan A. Thompson, newly-appointed head of the Department of Homeland Security; Dianne Epstein, Director of the CDC; Maynard Johnson, Director of FEMA; Linda Rivers, Director of the U.S. Red Cross Agency and Brigadier General Carmine DeBona, Chief of the U.S. Army Medical Research Institute of Infectious Diseases. Also attending were John B. Kelly, National Security Agency (NSA) Liaison to the

---

[1] The United States Senate, according to the United States Constitution, (Article I), is required to choose a President Pro Tempore (or, "president for a time," often shortened to President Pro Tem), who presides over the Senate in the absence of the Vice President. ... Since 1947, the President Pro Tempore of the Senate has been third in line to succeed to the US presidency in the case of death or resignation, after the Vice-President and the Speaker of the House of Representatives. (From Wikipedia, the free encyclopedia http://en.wikipedia.org)

President; James K. Matthews, FBI Special Agent to the White House; and Edward Pickings, the CIA Liaison Officer for the White House.

Speaker Albertson addressed the assembled group, stating that due to the gravity of the reports he had seen, he had determined that it would be in the best interests of all concerned if the group would provide him with information that he would then relay directly to the President for the sake and future of the nation.

Everyone realized that Albertson was grandstanding again, hoping to get his photo and comments in the newspapers, rather than expressing his genuine concern for the nation. It was not that he wasn't a patriot, of sorts, but his ego allowed few intrusions into his view of himself as some long-ago, sage Roman Senator and remarkable orator, though in actuality he was a Representative, not a Senator. Many others however, believed he was merely a self-aggrandizing blowhard, and you could never embarrass him or most of his colleagues for that matter, since they all viewed any criticism as either propaganda from the opposition or ignorant comments from the unknowing, unwashed, and uncomprehending public. After all, they held the purse strings of the country, and the classified intelligence reports they received were seen by very few people, a situation that gave those in office a sense of power and importance that far exceeded reality.

Barney blustered along for around five minutes, speaking in generalities and pleading for the support of those assembled for the safety of the nation and its people. When he finally ended his rant, he decided to go around the table to glean whatever he could from the participants. He began with Alan Thompson, the head of Homeland Security.

"Al, what do you have for us besides the usual elevated alerts and cautions? I mean, how prepared are your folks for any WMD events in any of our cities?"

Thompson replied, "Well sir, our people have been on standby and on overtime more often than I would like to recall, and that hits the states, the counties, and the local governments pretty hard in the pocketbook. Some are starting to complain that we are crying wolf too often. Also, a lot of the federal funds sent to some of the states, cities, and local governments have not been spent for their intended purpose. We've found a number of instances where protective gear, equipment, and medications have not been purchased as of this date, although some is supposed to be on order in various states, cities and regions."

Maynard Johnson, the FEMA head, concurred with Al Thompson's assessment and comments, adding that his budget was being stretched to the limits with the recent floods, tornadoes, and hurricanes, and that an attack of any major proportions would be certain to break his approved budget. He suggested that Congress should have funds made available on an emergency needs basis, as any delays in obtaining those funds would be a disaster for those affected states that counted on an immediate response from his agency.

At this point, every other agency head or representative agreed that this form of Congressional emergency funding approval was a necessary and very much overlooked requirement.

Albertson informed the committee members that he would ensure this need was reported to the President and to the Congress that day, ignoring the fact that the Senate Majority Leader was also present. More than a few eyes rolled upward, as though asking God's forgiveness in case they punched out the Representative from Kansas then and there, but all kept their true thoughts and feelings to themselves.

Albertson then inquired about the status of medications and vaccines from Dianne Epstein, the CDC Director. She replied at length.

"For biological attacks, we have four million medications on-hand in the form of Ciprofloxacin, or 'Cipro' for the laymen among us, in case of an Anthrax attack. We also have 2.5 million vials of Cidofovir, the potential remedy for smallpox, along with a smallpox vaccinia or vaccine, which is now produced in the form of a needle vaccine. We have another five million doses of this in storage throughout the nation. For plague, either Bubonic or pneumonic, the treatment is an antibiotic: Tetracycline for Bubonic plague and Streptomycin for Pneumonic plague. There are literally 200 to 300 million doses of these antibiotics in our hospitals and storage facilities. These are easily produced here in the US and are available in large quantities if required from neighboring countries. The only other major potential biological threat that has been determined is Botulism, which is mainly a form of food poisoning. We have 4.3 million doses of the antitoxin Connaught Trivalent Botulinal Antitoxin. Naturally, there are many others to consider, like Legionnaires Disease and such, but we are confident we can handle any immediate outbreaks with relative ease."

"As for a WMD radiation attack, we have enough medication for three quarters of our population in the form of NORAD anti-radiation potassium iodine tablets, which is the only medication that can be purchased without a doctor's prescription from the health food and grocery stores that carry it, along with and other vitamins, herb items, and holistic medications. With regard to chemical agents, we know they are hard to disperse and that sunlight will detoxify most of the mist agents. But for nerve agents or gases, we use the Atropine syringe, which is carried by most emergency medics for heart attacks. We have some 50 million Atropine doses available in our stocks. Blister agents, however, like the more commonly known ones such as Mustard, Lewisite and Phosgene, are treated by washing down the patient with uncontaminated water and then using Sodium Carbonate. That is abundant throughout the country, since it's a common household item. Other blister agent decontamination treatments include bleaches and caustic soda lye that can be used to dilute droplets or agents, but, of course, these should never be used on humans either internally or externally for any purpose. Probably the best method of getting rid of these droplets or agents, however, is with controlled fire applications on items or equipment, but again, never on humans."

She continued, "Blood chemical agents such as Hydrogen Cyanide, Cyanogens Chloride, or Arsine are best treated by washing down the patient with clean water, followed by an Amyl Nitrate Inhalant and an IV insertion, followed by a Sodium Nitrate IV, and then a Sodium Thiosulfate 1V. There really isn't a cure for blood or choking agents, other than attempting to rid the body of the agents through blood transfusions and using the Type IV fluids. In any situation, we have enough of these fluids both in hospitals and in storage to meet the needs of approximately one third of the U.S. population, if that need arises. So I think we are as prepared as we need to be at this time, at least from our overall CDC analysis."

The room was quiet for a few seconds before FBI Special Agent Matthews rose with a flushed and angry face and semi-shouted, "You mean to tell us that you don't have medications for nine-tenths, or two thirds in some cases, of the medications, antitoxins, and fluids needed for this nation for the worst forms of biological and chemical attacks?"

Dianne was flushed now herself, but she was going to teach this law enforcement hick a thing or two about diplomacy, tact, and how the U.S. government worked in proper circles. She began by saying, "Mr. Matthews" (pointedly not Agent Matthews), "do you understand that we purchase items such as medications for storage under the budget provided to us by Congress? Furthermore, do you understand that I also have a very large staff tasked with determining what a given outbreak might be, such as Ebola, Legionnaires Disease, Anthrax, and so forth, and that the funds to accomplish those tasks come out of the same pile of funds allowed us by Congress? And has it ever occurred to you that we must not only determine what to purchase and how much, but also where to store it, and then pay the costs of transporting and storing it as well? And have you considered that, like your FBI budget, it is never enough to purchase all that might be needed or wanted and that our staffs are also limited due to budget constraints?"

She took a breath and continued. "And has it ever occurred to you that we are inundated and overloaded with unrelenting and under-funded projects, yet each day we receive many more? Did you ever think that perhaps with this body of extremely bright and leading doctors in many different fields, we are doing the best we can with what we have and what is available to us? Whatever you may have thought in the past, we do not have a blank check to purchase the quantities of medications needed to provide protection for every single U.S. citizen, as much as we might like to do so. Now I hope that answers your undignified and unwarranted outburst, and we can now proceed with this meeting."

"No, I am not through," stated Agent Matthews. "You and I and everyone in this room know about the WMD document sent to all of us several years ago by a couple of concerned citizens. They wrote a 23-page document and made it available free to all Americans over the Internet. It explained all of these deficiencies and about alternative medications and even holistic medications that might be useful in case these agents are ever released. No governmental agency was allowed to even acknowledge it ever received their analysis, much less thank them for their suggestions and advice. They pointed out that some medications could be brought for pennies on the dollar from foreign countries (which would have benefited your limited budget), and that could be done with our own inspectors on-site, and then batch tested when they arrived here."

"They also pointed out in their report that we don't even make masks or protective clothing for infants and children here in the U.S., and we can only get small quantities of these from Israel, yet we haven't even bothered to look into that either. Furthermore, they also pointed out that our first responders were inadequately trained and prepared, and as mentioned earlier in these discussions, many of the funds for proper WMD equipment have been misspent or remain unused so far. Thus, we are unprepared as a nation for meeting even the first responders' needs, and now we are also crippled with a shortage of medications when we had a very long lead time in which to purchase and store the medications."

"How often did you and your staff approach Congress to request the need for supplemental budgets, or the shortages of quantities of medications needed? I checked once and it was a half-hearted attempt at best, and then it was practically all about pay raises and equipment, not needed medications! I have read the web sites from your agency and of the others here, and as that WMD document pointed out, they are all written for first responders, not for the general population.

If the public had a kit and the necessary information, many could care for themselves, which would lessen the burdens on the first responders. Yet, nothing is really offered for real medical treatment if they are slimed with a WMD agent, that is, other than to hope and wait for our unprepared government officials to intervene on their behalf. That document was a gift to us, and we all failed to use the common sense solutions it described for many of our present day failures, and which we find ourselves arguing about today."

When Agent Matthews paused, Dianne shot back. "First of all, your wonderful concerned citizens have neither the educations nor backgrounds to be making such assertions and claims, and they certainly do not know medicine and disease control or the needs of our citizens as do the PhD's and trained physicians of my staff. We do not intend to allow untrained civilians to play voodoo medicine man with themselves or other members of the public, as they are more apt to cause harm to themselves and others than do any real good.

Were we to suggest that civilians be allowed to purchase a kit as you call it, and then have all those medications floating around, well many might be stupid enough to practice with them, or use the wrong ones, or give the wrong dosages, and we would then all be liable for law suits."

Matthews replied, "So your concept is that avoiding possible future law suits, assuming there is much of a nation left afterwards, is preferable to advising and enlightening our citizens on how to protect themselves and their families?"

With daggers shooting from her eyes, Dianne replied, "If that's how you wish to word it that is precisely what I mean."

"OK, Ms. Epstein," Matthews said, "have you ever considered that many of our first responders will leave their posts and take their families to safe havens, before even worrying about their jobs?" Epstein responded, "That's not my job or area of concern, and I do not appreciate your tone of voice."

Matthews started to reply, but was cut off by Albertson, who said, "That's enough, you have all made your points, and I have noted them down to present to the President, and we will let him decide what to do next."

He continued, "This meeting is taking more time than was planned, and I know you all have other duties to attend to, so I'll ask for a parting statement that will probably reach the President tonight, if anyone has anything to add."

Brigadier General Carmine DeBona, Chief of the Army Medical Research Institute of Infectious Diseases, raised his hand to be acknowledged. He stated, "I have to agree with Agent Matthews, although Dianne has some very valid points regarding budget constraints, whatever our reasoning or excuses of the past. I believe that by now we should have purchased all the needed medications from overseas, as was suggested in the document submitted by those concerned citizens, and that civilians should be allowed to protect themselves with both medications and knowledge, particularly when we–the government–are simply unable to do it on a national scale. Our citizens' safety and welfare should remain our primary concerns, particularly in these perilous times, and especially with our unsure knowledge of what might occur and how difficult it might be to save millions of our citizens."

Dianne stood up to upbraid her medical colleague, but Barney Albertson waved her off. He then adjourned the meeting after getting a copy of the aforementioned WMD document from Agent Matthews, and he returned to his congressional office with a very large smile on his face. He was now in the cat bird seat: he would brief the President and watch him pale, since whichever way Warrington decided on the various issues, Barney could and would proclaim that he had personally briefed the President on these issues. No matter which way it ended up, he would always take the high road, even though he and his colleagues in the House and counterparts in the Senate had, more often than not, voted down emergency appropriation supplementals for all the agencies in the past.

To Barney, it was all water under the bridge, and now he would have the President where he really wanted him. Although they were both from the same political party, Barney really wanted the President's office for himself, and he had noticed a stark change lately in the President's confidence and health, as the anticipated date of the terrorist attacks neared.

Senator Pelerine, the Senate Majority Leader, had not said a word during the meeting and had listened in fear and astonishment at the lack of preparedness of the nation's leaders, as she now realized that her own family and her own personal safety rested with these people who seemed to be very much at odds with one another.

Chapter 7 – The Attack Diversions

7 September 2005

Like all military planning, no mater how precise and calculated, once a plan is activated then the inevitable unintended consequences seem to materialize almost overnight, and seemingly without rhyme or reason. Colonel Wu and General Chang heard of the smallpox outbreaks in Tijuana, Mexico, on the September 7th evening news along with the rest of the country, and had to make the difficult decision about whether or not to proceed with the scheduled attacks, or wait until all the fuss had died down and the Americans were again complacent, and unaware of the other pending dangers.

After going through their list of pros and cons, they concluded that they must proceed with the September 11 attacks, the originally planned date. Otherwise, there was greater chance for discovery, such as another idiotic loss of weapons like what had happened in Mexico, or an unlucky discovery by U.S. officials, or even from a Latino or Muslim terrorist saying too much or bragging too soon outside of their designated cells.

So, September 11th remained the date for the WMD events, and at that point there would be no turning back. These Chinese officers would not be responsible for the subsequent events, since the Chinese High Command would assume responsibility for the coming war decisions and related actions. With any luck, the officers thought, the Americans would be extremely frightened and accept defeat after the initial attacks, but if not, future attacks would make WWII look like a trifling occurrence. This was because the rapid fall and surrender of America would change the course of all subsequent world events, and the Chinese would finally attain their special place in the eyes of the world. There were still the fanatical and ignorant Muslims to contend with, but the Chinese would not slap their hands as the Americans had done in the past. In fact, the vocal or resisting Muslims would either all be dead in the end, or else become semi-slaves to their new Chinese masters.

8 September 2005

The Texas-Louisiana Border

On September 8th, three days before the scheduled attacks, a very inquisitive Texas State Trooper stopped a Mexican truck laden with propane tanks which was heading East on U.S. Highway 10 towards the Louisiana border. It was about to lose its left rear tire, which was wobbling as if it was about ready to fall off. The trooper pulled the Mexican driver off to the shoulder of the road and began to question him. The driver, feigning that he couldn't speak English, was surprised to hear the tall, blond and Irish-American looking trooper reply in very fluent Spanish. The driver then had little choice but to provide the required documents for his license, the cargo load, and the cargo destination.

Manuel Reyes, the driver, started saying a few small prayers as he was old and this was his last run to Florida from Mexico via Texas. For his good services, he was supposed to be paid the six-month's pay he'd been promised plus an additional $400 U.S. dollars. Manuel suspected he might be running drugs in the propane containers, but like

Paco, he had never asked and never really wanted to know the truth about his cargo. After all, who would pay a half-year's wages for such a run if it weren't illegal?

The young trooper had just heard in that morning's briefing that a propane factory in Mexico was being investigated as the possible source of the smallpox outbreak, but the driver's gas receipts and the loading factory were far from the Tijuana plant. Yet, to the trooper, it made no sense to haul propane from Mexico to Florida through Mexico, Texas, Louisiana, and even Alabama, as there were many refineries and propane plants in each of those states. And while it might be more cheaply produced in Mexico, the distance involved from Mexico to Florida and the price of gas in the U.S. right now would have made the trip a very unprofitable venture, no matter how one looked at it. The Trooper voiced his suspicions over his police radio, and backup soon arrived in the form of more troopers, HAZMAT officials, and even police forensic officials. It did not take them long to locate and question the newer labeling and writing on the one container, which was immediately sent to government laboratories for further examination.

The Trooper arrested Manuel, booked him, and then entered the small cell alone with the prisoner. Some illegal arm and finger twisting made the terrified driver reveal all he knew about his drop-off points, the plant pickup routine, fellow drivers, and much more. In short order the FBI, CIA, DIA, NSA, and other agency officials were also in on the questioning, and by the next day the plants, laboratories, and drop-off points were being located and raided. The young State Trooper, whose sound instincts were responsible for Jacksonville not being subjected to a smallpox attack, later received a commendation for his field work.

The small pox clandestine operations were all but shut down by the end of the day on September 9th, that is, except for very small vials of smallpox still in the hands of Muslim terrorists in Canada and in the three large cities - unbeknownst to U.S. officials. Fortunately, Major General Chang and Colonel Wu were also quite unaware of these so-far unpublicized U.S. discovery operations.

By now, law enforcement officials now had the proverbial gloves off, regardless of future national or international consequences, as the lives of thousands or even millions of American citizens depended on their ability to gather and process information as quickly as possible. One way or another, the newly-captured terrorists were going to talk, and talk they did over the next 8 hours. The officials determined that the propane plants were owned by Mexican citizens, but all the key engineers and foremen were Chinese or of Chinese decent.

The Chinese employees were harder to break than the Mexicans and the other Latinos, even though none had been in the Chinese armed forces but they still feared for their lives from their countrymen and still refused to talk. That is, they refused until told the U.S. would nuke their own hometowns. That worked, and they revealed that their main points of contact were the United Nations Chinese Representatives, Wu and Chang.

The CIA was immediately tasked to apprehend the two Chinese officials and surrounded them a day later, on September 10th, just outside the UN offices and enjoying a meal in a Mexican restaurant. Unfortunately, when they realized they were about to be apprehended, the officers each broke the cyanide capsule they had quickly popped into their mouths and died before the authorities were able to question them about their other plans. They both died quickly but painfully, sitting over their half-eaten enchilada and taco meals, realizing with their last breaths that they would not get to see the final results of all their careful planning. Unfortunately for America, the plan went ahead and on schedule.

When the word leaked out about the Chinese delegates, there were protests from some UN members, but these were virtually ignored by the media and the U.S. government, which by then had much more important things on its collective mind.

11 September 2005

San Diego, California

The first diversion attack began on the West Coast in San Diego at dawn on the morning of September 11th. Latino terrorists set brush fires outside the city, which sent the first responders–firemen, policemen, and EMS personnel–along with a contingent of Marines and Sailors from the nearby military bases to deal with it. This exodus allowed the other Latino cell members to place a mixture of smallpox, bubonic plague, and anthrax into the air conditioning and heating systems of a number of hospitals, fire stations, police stations, and even shopping malls. Some of the resultant deaths were nearly instantaneous for those who received the first potent mixtures, and literally thousands soon reported in sick and started going to the hospitals and clinics. An investigation quickly determined that airborne agents were the source of these sudden illnesses, and that the contaminated air conditioning and air filtration systems found at the various locations were spreading the agents. Those areas that could not be quickly decontaminated were simply burned to the ground to kill the remaining spores. Unfortunately, doctors and nurses who had not been contaminated were short of protective gear, and medications to treat these agents were found to be in short supply.

Upon hearing the news, the first responders were torn between their duty to put out the fires and their urgent desire to return to the city to respond to the biological attack. Some panicked and raced home to their loved ones, packed them up and headed out of the region as fast as they could. It was soon evident that a mixture of various biological and chemical agents had been used, and that it would take several days to sort out the mixtures and then determine the proper medication procedures and doses.

By this time, the smallpox epidemic had already spread like wildfire in the San Diego area from the unstoppable groups of infected Mexicans streaming over the border. In fact, the day before the diversion attacks started, the U.S. military, the Border Patrol, and local County and City Police were given the horrific orders to start shooting illegal aliens, looters, and anyone who failed to obey their orders. Chaos and lawlessness were rampant in San Diego, as highways and all means of travel were being blocked to prevent the spread of the various contaminants and communicable diseases.

The pest control truck was discovered by a couple of kids playing hooky from school. When they saw that the driver looked dead, they ran for help. It appeared that the driver had been trying to get the poorly-maintained motor to work; in his frustration, he'd hit the small engine several times with a large wrench, accidentally loosening a hose he was leaning on. That had released very small quantities of VX gas around him, and he had died quickly, without properly understanding what had occurred. The responders realized that San Diego had been spared from the planned VX gas attack by a careless and unlucky terrorist.

Houston, Texas

Houston, Texas, was hit with similar disasters at morning rush hour, several hours after the San Diego attacks. The attacks there also began with fires started at different forested areas around the outskirts of the city and along the inland shipping channel that ran some 50 miles from the city out to the Gulf of Mexico.

The first responders reacted just like those in San Diego had, and again the biological agents were placed in some of the now-empty fire stations, hospitals and clinics. However, the police nightshift, having heard of the earlier San Diego attacks, decided to protect their own buildings with SWAT Team snipers, who killed six and wounded four more of the terrorists before they could complete their mission.

These captured, wounded terrorists were severely tortured to gain the needed information about their comrades, but they were unaware of the activities of those outside their own cell. However, the similarity of their methods to those used in San Diego caused U.S. officials to send out a national call to protect those types of public facilities everywhere around the country, and in order to prevent the first responders from charging off to the diversionary fires.

Vigilante civilian groups caught several more terrorists at the targeted buildings in Houston before they could complete their missions, and some died very painful deaths at the hands of the vigilantes. Unfortunately, a few still managed to complete their missions and caused many casualties in and around the hospitals, clinics and fire stations. Although, they avoided the police stations in Houston, since the terrorists had now decided to avoid places where armed men were certain to be found.

The terrorists' original target in the Southwest had been San Antonio, Texas, home to five military bases. From the Chinese planners' perspective, it had seemed a good target. But a few days before the attacks were due to begin, a Latino terrorist had noticed a Texas Monthly magazine on a store rack that included an article by one S.C. Gwynne, a well-known American anti-terrorist writer, about what would happen if Houston became the target of a terrorist attack.

The article revealed that along the 50-mile Houston shipping channel, there were more explosive materials, toxic gases, and deadly petrochemicals than anywhere else in the U.S., which was why most security experts agreed that it was a target-rich environment for terrorists and other enemies of the U.S. The Latino terrorist further learned that the banks along the Houston shipping channel were the sites for over 300 chemical and petroleum plants, making it one of the largest concentrations of heavy industry on earth, and that nearly half of the nation's supply of gasoline and half of its petrochemicals were produced and shipped from there. This small and concentrated area, while a key location for the nation's petrochemical industry, was also home to unfathomably large quantities of the deadliest, most easily combustible, disease-causing, lung-exploding, chromosome annihilating, and metal-dissolving substances known to man. The sheer toxicity of it all was why the channel had developed as it had since the 1920s, when the area had a very small population consisting mainly of plant workers and officials.

The terrorist immediately contacted his cell leader to try to convince him that Houston was a much better target and was bound to produce more casualties, since it had more than double the population of San Antonio and thus logically should produce more casualties. After many communication exchanges with their Red Chinese counterparts, the Latino terrorists finally convinced the Chinese leaders to change the target to Houston. However, this left less time for planning and preparations.

The Latino terrorists had acquired some out-of-date weaponry from Mexican drug dealers and others with questionable occupations, and they had ended up with an assortment of older weapons. These included several machine guns with very limited amounts of ammunition, and one Vietnam-era 60mm mortar with 15 rounds of high explosive ammunition. They decided they would fire the mortar at some of the chemical and petroleum plants along the channel by moving along the roadway from one plant to the next. They expected that the blasts would set off fires and explosions at the adjacent plants, and in turn causing havoc inside of them and eventually releasing the large quantities of chlorine gases stored in the numerous 650 ton storage tanks. Surely, they thought, the winds would eventually carry these gases towards the Houston city center, and the casualties would soon mount into the tens of thousands.

What the terrorists did not count on was that the Americans were also aware of this target-rich environment, and had placed there some of the best and most well-trained security and safety responders in the U.S., who were available and prepared for just these types of attacks. So as some of the terrorists attempted to enter the restricted areas to initiate their Houston attack on September 11th, they were quickly picked up by thermal imaging and other surveillance cameras and either rounded up and captured, or killed on the spot. Though major damage to Houston and the petrochemical industries was thus avoided, the few terrorists who got through and were able to plant the WMD agents did manage to cause hundreds of deaths. Over two thousand people eventually required hospitalization or other medical treatments there.

While all this was occurring two older retired Marines, Major Jim Stone and CWO-4 Frank Monroe, old buddies from the Vietnam War were on their way to their favorite quail and dove hunting grounds, not too far from the Houston channel shipping area. With Jim driving, they were still on the main highway and nearing a large Mobil Petroleum Chemical plant when they noticed a passenger van and a pest control truck parked off the road. The vehicles were partially hidden in the woods with some sloppy camouflage strewn about them, as though they wouldn't be there for very long. The retired Marines also noticed some men around the van who appeared to be setting up a short metal tube into a metal base plate on the ground. Both vets immediately recognized the 60mm mortar, an item they had often seen and used in that long ago war.

Jim stayed on the highway, but did a U-turn at the first available spot, cutting across the grassy area separating the two double lane roads. As he executed this maneuver, they were both thinking that they were getting fairly old and might be seeing things that weren't real. Jim moved close enough to the vehicles not to be seen from the curve in the road and the tall grass, and then parked on the shoulder of the road with his flashing lights turned on. He then said, "If they've got the mortar I think they have, it's got to be for shooting at the petrochemical plant." Frank agreed, and said they'd better be armed if they were right about this very odd situation.

Lifting the covered back of their truck, they ignored the shotguns they had planned to use for hunting doves and instead loaded their favorite deer rifles, which they had planned to zero in again for the coming deer season. They loaded their weapons, each also taking a sidearm that they kept in the truck for target shooting and a set of binoculars. They quietly snuck up the side of the road until they saw a small mound covered with grass high enough to hide in and remain camouflaged with their hunting gear. Jim peeked over the high grass looking through his binoculars and whispered that yes, it was a mortar, and they were stacking rounds next to the weapon!

Meanwhile, Frank was calling 911 to notify the police of their situation and location, and what was about to occur. Frank didn't know why he asked, maybe it was an old military habit, but he asked permission to take out the men if they fired the mortar. The Watch Commander, overhearing the conversation at the police station and knowing that none of his men could get there in time, asked if they were military trained, and Frank said, "Hell yeah, we're Vietnam vets with a lot of trigger time." The Watch

Commander hesitated, and then asked, "Who are you?" Frank said, "Dammit, we haven't much time, we're CWO Frank Monroe and Major Jim Stone, USMC retired."

The Commander replied, "Hold them off if you can, my men are on the way, but don't let them fire a round at the plant, or you'll have the largest damn explosions you've ever heard." "Roger that," replied Frank, "but you're wrong on your last." Jim had heard enough of the conversation to know they had an official OK, and told Frank that he'd used his range finder to determine that the target distance, which was at 300 yards, no wind, and straight shots. They locked, loaded and sighted in through their scopes.

The other men were now taking increments off the mortar rounds to accommodate the distance to their target, which was much shorter than the weapon's maximum range. The Marines began the slow in and out breathing routine taught them long, long, ago at the Marine Recruit Training Depot. Observing that one man seemed ready to drop the first round down the tube, Jim said "Now."

The man with the round in his hand spun around, and the man waiting with the next mortar round fell backwards as though lifted off the ground, both with through and through headshots. The other men ran for their guns, but in seconds, two more were dead, and only two remained. The fifth man was killed hiding under the truck, aiming his rifle in the direction of the incoming shots, but his head exploded before he got the first shot off.

Seeing the driver of the pest control truck scurry back to start up the engine, Frank shot him on the run. The man tumbled off the driver's compartment, holding his chest with both hands. Frank took aim for another shot, but Jim said, "No, we need a prisoner to tell us who they are."

Scanning the area with their scopes, they saw no more movement other than the wounded pest control driver, but they separated anyway before moving towards the trucks, mortar, dead men, and the wounded man.

While Frank guarded the crying, wounded driver, Jim checked each fallen man to insure no one was playing possum. He then scouted in a circle around their position before giving Frank the all clear thumbs up sign. They could hear the sirens of the police, medics and firemen in the distance, and then heard a different whistle sound coming from the plant, which they surmised was the "abandon plant" signal. When they looked again at their moaning and crying prisoner, they noticed he was losing a lot of blood and air from his lung, so Jim took the sleeve from his cigarette pack, placed it on the right breast wound that was noisily leaking air, and then asked for Frank's plastic sleeve, which he placed on the back exit wound. They found a dirty but usable piece of cloth to tie around the man's body to hold the plastic sleeves in place.

By the time the police and others arrived, Frank and Jim were arguing over whom was the better shot. Frank lost, both by virtue of rank and by the fact that he had a wounded man, while Jim had scored kills on all his shots. As the medics neared the scene of carnage, Frank went back to the wounded prisoner while Jim explained what had happened. Frank held the wounded man's hand as though to comfort him, then pulled his middle finger backwards at a 120-degree angle, saying quietly, "What's in the truck?" The wounded Latino terrorist, thinking he was dying anyway, sputtered, "VX gas." The words were loud enough for most to hear, and most, including the police officers, turned very pale, as though the blood had just drained from their bodies.

The Marines had to turn their deer rifles over to the police, but were allowed to leave after promising to provide the police with a written statement later. As they climbed the small gully towards their truck, one of the policemen, not too sure of those old coots' stability after such an incident, shouted, "Where are you going?", thinking home or a bar would be the normal response, Jim shouted back without turning around, "Quail hunting, we still got our shotguns!" The others just shook their heads in disbelief.

One of the medics then commented as they watched the two old men walk away, "Jesus, did you notice they were all head shots, except the wounded man who was running?" "Yep," said the senior police officer, "just be glad they're on our side." What none of them knew was that both old men had been wounded in combat, and the Chief Warrant Officer had killed over 118 enemy troops by himself. He was awarded the Navy Cross for Valor for that one engagement; and he had later returned to Vietnam as an Interrogator/translator. The Major had commanded an infantry platoon and a rifle company in Vietnam, followed by a short tour there as an advisor, and he had also killed his share of enemy troops. They held each other in high esteem and respect, but would never let on, as they always seemed to be kidding each other or calling one another bad names. But they knew, and so did their families and friends.

Jacksonville, Florida

By noon that day, Jacksonville, Florida, was on alert after hearing of the other two cities being attacked, as were other large cities around the country, but so were the terrorists assigned to perpetrate the attacks there and they decided to advance their original schedule from evening rush hour by several hours. They began the attacks just as schools were letting out, starting again with the fires on the outskirts of the city, and followed by attempts to reach the hospital, fire, police, and clinic buildings. But the locals were ready for them now, and all but three terrorists were caught or killed before completing their missions.

Outside the city, the pest control truck driver was trying to get into a position where the winds would carry the VX gas towards the inner city, but the winds kept shifting; no matter where he parked, the winds seemed to change towards the sea at each attempted placement. Finally, the truck driver gave up and told the driver of the car assigned to follow him that he would turn the gas on now, and even if it did not go downtown as planned, it was bound to contaminate enough of an area as to cause much immediate death and many more casualties.

He parked the truck in a wooded area near where the fires were burning, turned on the pump engine, injected an atropine needle into his leg to counter the effects of the VX gas, and ran for the waiting car. They sped off the side of the road heading for Savannah, Georgia, where a fishing boat would take the truck driver towards Puerto Rico and then turn south at the last minute with a new heading for Cuba. He envisioned that he might become a national hero for his exploits in America. But fate was never on his side, as he would have been killed long before he got to Cuba, since, quite frankly, he knew too much. In fact, he never made it to Savannah, either, because when the driver of the car hurriedly pulled out onto the main road, he failed to see a speeding cement truck that sent them spinning and rolling over and over, killing both men. The cement truck driver had been told to get to the Navy base with his load as quickly as possible and not to worry about the cops, because whatever they were doing with the cement at the base had a high naval priority.

The dead men would later be tied to the pest control truck, but by then it was too late for Jacksonville, as the winds had changed again and the deadly VX gas was heading for the downtown area. The truck motor had been running for close to an hour before it was discovered and the ingredients analyzed as VX gas. Several Florida policemen and several civilians died while trying to shut down the motor that was still spewing the clouds of VX gas.

A late afternoon rain helped put out the fires, but the gas release and the biological weapons–spread by the three cell members who had completed their missions–had accomplished their horrible deeds, and the suffering was now just beginning.

Jacksonville had one more surprise waiting to rear its ugly head, and that was that an extra agent which had been added to the biological agent mix previously used in San Diego and Houston. It would soon prove to be more devastating than the original agent mixes delivered to the other two cities.

Chapter 8 – The Second War Room Meeting

11 September 2005 - Cheyenne Mountain, Wyoming

The anticipation of the impending attacks was over, as they had begun with a vengeance across the Southern states of California, Texas, and Florida. The American military was on alert for a possible war with both China and Iraq, and possibly with other nations that were either supporting the terrorists or assisting them in some fashion. The President was meeting late that same day of the attacks with his entire staff, his Cabinet Secretaries, agency officials and the Chairman of the Joint Chiefs.

The grim meeting had initially been planned for earlier in the afternoon, at the not-so-secret bunkers that had been built into the hillsides of the state of Virginia, but the Secret Service changed its location at the last minute to the large, secure underground caves built into the side of the hills in Wyoming, some four hours flying time from Washington D. C. The entire group was meeting in a large conference room set aside for the anticipated and numerous non-military guests, who could be housed and fed there in case of a national emergency.

The President, normally viewed as a weak man for changing his position according to whichever way the polls read, now appeared almost Presidential and stoic. His jaw jutted out in a determined fashion never seen before, and he had an almost commanding presence and posture. He appeared both angry and reflective, occasionally smiling in a non-meaningful way, as though he now understood what he had previously failed to understand. With almost a drill instructor's voice, he commanded, "Let's get started, we have much to cover in this meeting." The Vice President, in turn, looked pale–as though the blood had been removed from his body–and appeared to be very shaken by the events of the past few days. His face twitched at awkward times, as though he had little control of his facial muscles.

Attending this meeting were the same individuals who had met with the President and Vice President on September 1st. Present again were members of the Joint Chiefs of Staff and the heads and directors of the various directorates and agencies of the Department of Homeland Security and the Department of Health and Human Services: Alan (Al) Thompson, DHS Secretary; Maynard Johnson, Director of FEMA in DHS; and Dianne Epstein, Director of the Centers for Disease Control and Prevention in HHS.

Also present were Brigadier General Carmine DeBona, USA, Chief of the U.S. Army Medical Research Institute of Infectious Diseases, Fort Detrick, Maryland; Linda Rivers, Director of the American Red Cross, the private emergency response organization; the President Pro Tem of the Senate, Susan Pelerine, and her counterpart Barney Albertson, Speaker of the House of Representatives. Rounding out the rest of the group were the President's staff and the intelligence and security agency liaisons, including Ralph Cutting, Chief of Staff; Kathy Burgess, speech writer; Erika Shultz, Press Secretary; Phillip Mogates, Head of the Secret Service detail; John Kelly, NSA liaison to the President; James K. Mathews, FBI liaison officer, and Edward Pickings, CIA liaison representative.

The President turned to Al Thompson, DHS head, and said, "OK, Al, where are we at this stage?"

Thompson stood and replied, "Sir, the situation is well in hand at this point. We've captured a number of terrorists either through our law enforcement agencies, our CIA and NSA operatives, or by civilians getting to them before the law does, and we seem to have regained control of this situation concerning the terrorists. Naturally, I cannot speak for the other agencies, but they now seem to be regaining control of the medical needs in the three cities that were attacked, and we think we will have all of that under control within the next couple of weeks. We do have some resistance from citizens trying to leave the contaminated areas, but we have been able to stem a mass exodus of the local populations through our local law enforcement, National Guard, and first responder team containment efforts. We are getting some very irate calls from citizens and local officials, as well as from medical personnel, to at least allow them to evacuate their family members, but as you know, that is impossible or we would soon encounter both panic and rebellion."

"So far, many in those locations are so numbed and too scared to move that we are able to manage them reasonably well. We have had a few instances of looters being shot or arrested, but that also seems to be limited and contained to small groups of teenagers or criminals. We know we haven't captured all the terrorists, but reports keep arriving on an almost hourly basis, and they are being picked up as quickly as possible. I'll leave that part of the briefing to the other agencies."

"In short, Mr. President, we seem to be getting a grip on these terrorists and the damage they have caused, and we continue to track down the remnants throughout our nation. As you know by now, we were even able to find the two top leaders, a couple of Chinese Red Army officers, though unfortunately, they committed suicide before our agents could interrogate them about the rest of their plans."

"We've cancelled all flights in and out of the country, unless they're approved by the various agency representatives. All flights are being checked very thoroughly, because our assets can now be better concentrated on the few flights that we have approved. Unless anybody has any further questions, this is my update for the present time."

Nobody responded; the President nodded, and Al took his seat.

The President then turned to Dianne Epstein, Director of the CDC, and said, "OK, Dianne, you're next." Dianne no longer exuded the air of confidence and aloofness that was her normal hallmark, especially in a room full of mostly male counterparts. Today she appeared worn, pale, and in need of a good night's rest. Like all the others, Dianne had been working around the clock, but her suit was wrinkled and appeared to have been slept in, which was the opposite of her usual appearance in a new suit or new outfit at every meeting. She started to rise, then thought better of it, as she was feeling a bit light headed, and decided to brief from her seated position.

She began, "Mr. President, we have been working as fast and as hard as humanly possible to get the Hazmat teams and medications to the contaminated areas. The execution of our plans has worked as intended, with the exception at some of the minor distribution locations here and there. Sometimes the areas we had planned to use from the planning practice phases turned out to be too contaminated, and so we had to use secondary or even tertiary distribution sites, which delayed the arrival of medications to the new sites. In many cases, the state and local officials failed to erect signs with directions to the open area morgue sites, to the hospitals and clinics being utilized, or to the alternative food, water and clothing distribution sites. This delayed our drivers, medical teams, and mobile laboratories from arriving on time to their new locations."

She continued, "Additionally, the locals wanted to re-inspect our people and the deliveries for fear that our people might be terrorists, since they weren't headed for the original distribution points. Perhaps equally disheartening was that we found most of the first responders with improper or no protective equipment, and most were without even gas masks. For some who had masks, many were the wrong size - either too large or too small, which made many of them of questionable value and use. Worse, we found most hospital staff members without any protective suits or masks, as each major hospital had only purchased a few for normal emergencies. We fear many of the hospital staffs and doctors will soon come down with the symptoms they will assuredly be encountering with the numbers of patients being handled. Therefore, we have arranged for doctors, nurses, and other medical professionals from the nearby surrounding states to be issued the proper protective equipment, and we are now training them in the use and need for these items, as well as the proper medication and doses required for the differing illnesses."

"The clinics in the three cities, along with the practitioners and assistants, are in even worse shape, since they work off more limited budgets and never even attempted to purchase protective gear or the type of medications now needed so desperately. We have contacted all our medical suppliers, and they are all on 24-hour shifts to prepare and ship the needed medications on special USAF and Navy Cargo flights from overseas or stateside military bases, and to keep the needed supplies arriving in a steady stream. Some flights have already arrived at San Diego and Jacksonville, and we expect the first group of USAF medical aircraft to arrive within the hour into the Houston airport and the San Antonio military bases, as well."

She went on, "Many of the contaminated illegal Mexican immigrants have fled back to Mexico, as our law enforcement and military units were unable to stem the flow of illegal immigrants–who are Mexican citizens after all–from returning to Mexico. This will create another problem, as the spread of disease and illness will soon hit Mexico hard, and we expect that the contaminated ones will soon seek help back here in the U.S., and so we are expecting a reverse flow very soon. Our supply of medications for the various conditions is holding out well so far, and if this is the end of the attacks, then we'll be able to stabilize most patients within two to three weeks, God willing."

Plowing ahead, Diane said, "San Diego has a population of over a million residents, Houston has over two million, and Jacksonville has about three quarters of a million residents. In all three cities, we believe that at least one third of their population is contaminated by now, and we expect that number to rise to about one half of their population; of that group, about one third will die or be permanently incapacitated, primarily due to overexposure to the combination of the WMD agents. We expect most of the deaths to be among infants, children, and older people, since their immune systems are less able to fight off the toxic agents. Therefore, we have directed that some of the more scarce medications have priority for healthy adults, as opposed to the younger and older patients."

"What all this means is that we should anticipate casualties ranging from 200-300,000 in San Diego, maybe as high as 500,00-750,000 in Houston, and about 200,000 in Jacksonville. We have authorized burning the corpses in pyres, as the facilities to handle this large a number of casualties simply do not exist in any of the cities, or even in their surrounding suburbs and smaller cities. The football and baseball stadiums and other large open facilities, including large farms, are being used as disposal locations for the dead."

Diane paused for breath, and then continued. "While we have sufficient medications to handle our present needs, we will require approval of emergency funding now estimated to be in the 60 billion dollar range, to restock and have ample supplies in case of further attacks. Even if that were to occur, then further additional funding would be required at some future date."

"This is the most difficult report I have ever had to make, and I hope you all understand that I, too, am grieving for all our losses, but we must continue to save those we still can. We determined it was best to send out all our teams into the three cities that have been attacked, as that is where they are needed most, at least for now. I have nothing more to report unless someone has any questions."

President Warrington nodded sadly at Dianne and turned to look for the next speaker, when Vice President Dan McLaughlin, now wild eyed and seemingly going out of control, blurted out, "Do you mean there are no teams to protect the nation's Capital, or Maryland, or even in Virginia?"

The President, looking at him with a mixture of sadness and disappointment, said, "Dan, get a hold of yourself. Those teams have their own stand-by aircraft to traverse our nation as needed. Since we don't know where or when new attacks may occur, I authorized the deployment of the teams to the attacked cities. Now, please be quiet and stop interfering with the briefings." The Vice President appeared shocked at the rebuke and fell silent, but he visibly became boiling mad at being treated like a schoolboy in front of the others. He sat simmering silently and slowly, as the other speakers began their portions of the briefings.

The rest of the briefings, from the Transportation Secretary to the Treasury Secretary, provided little new information of major concern. The Secretary of State then gave his report. "The UN delegations have not slipped out of the country, and in fact, they are presently meeting in New York City, which my staff has determined means that they are either unaware of any further attacks, or are simply not concerned with any attacks in New York City. The only delegations missing at the UN are those of the Chinese and Iranians, and they have gone to their respective embassies in Washington, D.C., for consultations."

"Furthermore, since we received the reports of the first attack on the West Coast, there have been constant and frequent exchanges of information between my representatives and those of all of the other major nations in the Security Council, as well as many others such as India, Pakistan, Japan, etc. It should also be noted that most nations are hedging on sending supplies, equipment, and manpower until they have a clearer picture that will help them to insure they send the correct mix of assistance. They also all appear to be waiting for the future possibilities of any further attacks on the U.S., or even on their own nations, and seem intent to keep what they might need for themselves. Thus, nations who previously provided us with pharmaceuticals are only committing to sending smaller amounts than previously agreed to in our past emergency negotiations. That's all I have now, Mr. President."

The President then said, "I concluded as much from my own conversations with the various national leaders. It appears that the Republicans' contention about not trusting these bastards was correct all along."

At this point, Dan McLaughlin exploded as he stood up and shouted at the President, "You are a traitor, you are betraying all we stand for and believe in. Everything we sought to do to bring peace and a new world order is being tossed out the window by these insane suggestions that our allies have betrayed us." Everyone was too startled to comment immediately, and in the pause he continued in a high-pitched voice, "General Paxton, I suppose you and your military cohorts are ready to destroy China and Iran, and any others you think might be behind these attacks, is that right?"

Paxton stood and said, "That is essentially correct, we have special weapons heretofore unknown to the public or even to you, sir, which will remove the submarine threats and neutralize the missile threats from Iran and China. These weapons use radio wave technology, which you

94

voted against often enough. We were able to place that program into the "black" budget to continue our research and development efforts, and we have now proven that it works perfectly. The hostile submarine crews will be killed in place before they can ever use their weapons. As for the missiles, we have perfected numerous, extremely powerful laser rays, and through the use of satellites and other weapons systems, again something you voted against, we can now destroy the missiles on their pads or in flight. Does that answer your question?"

McLaughlin was now beside himself, sputtering and spitting with venomous, almost hysterical, shouting, "You people have gone mad, you are trying to start a world war! I will be no part of this craziness; you have betrayed the American people and the United Nations as well! I resign as Vice President and will not be a part of this insanity. I'll leave this meeting now and tell the world of your evil and sadistic plans. I'll see to it that you're all tried as war criminals and I'll laugh as they hang you. I'll tell the world... I will." But by now, he was blubbering and could speak no more. He simply stood with glazed eyes and a look of incomprehension on his face.

The President rose, motioning for the following members to come to his side–his Press Secretary, Erika Schultz; the Chief of Staff, Ralph Cutting; Kathy Burgess, his speech writer; and the head of the Secret Service, Phillip Mogates–and spoke quietly to them. He told Secret Service Head Mogates to remove the Vice President and take him directly to the mental ward at Bethesda Naval Hospital. McLaughlin was to be checked over, but was to remain there incommunicado. To the others in the group, he said they were to write up a notice to the public that the Vice President had suffered a nervous breakdown and would remain incommunicado to the public for the time being, and that his condition was so very severe, as to consider the possibility of designating his replacement in this hour of need.

He sent them off to perform their assigned tasks and then motioned the Speaker of the House and the President Pro Tem to his side. Barney Albertson's first thought was that this was what he had always been seeking. As the VP, he just might be able to someday ease himself into the President's chair without too much effort. But now he began to have second thoughts that he might not be up to being a wartime VP, much less a President. He viewed himself as a sort of glib Bill Clinton type, familiar with all the social and cultural issues, but often avoiding the more difficult-to-understand military and international issues. In reality, Albertson knew he was nothing more than a political glad-hander, a "BS" artist, a man with a large ego but little true knowledge of the world, and a lack of self-fortitude. So, when the President suggested that he might prepare himself to assume the duties of Vice President, Barney heard himself decline the offer. He saved his pride by suggesting that he would be better able to help the nation in his present position.

Susan Pelerine, the Senate Majority Leader and President Pro Tem, heard Barney's answer with delight and suggested that at different times in the nation's history, a disabled or impeached Vice President was replaced by a Congressional vote, then later by the President Pro Tem of the Senate, and, more recently under President Truman, by the Speaker of the House. This was an issue that could quickly be resolved: Barney obviously did not want the job, the present incumbent was too ill to remain in the position, and she was willing to accept the position.

The President replied in a loud voice for all to hear, "Ms. Pelerine, I appreciate your offer to assume the role of Vice President, but that's not what I want. We are in a war for our very survival as a nation and as a people. You have spent most of your life supporting not only liberal causes, but our known enemies, as well. Therefore, I cannot in good conscience support your bid for the Vice Presidency. I supported you in the past for the benefit of my own political career, but not because I liked you or believed in most of the distortions and outright falsehoods that you have promoted over many years. It took this situation for me to fully understand how wrong I have been for the past 40 plus years. But, I now know what is vital and what is at stake, and I need a partner who agrees with my changed views and not someone who will oppose all I attempt to do. I submit that your views are more in line with the current Vice President's than with mine, and so, you will not be under consideration for that important position. Am I quite clear?"

Quite taken aback, Susan replied, "I am quite clear, but I will oppose you and your kind from my Senate seat until my last breath."

Warrington mulled that over for a minute, then said, "Ms. Pelerine, as I said before, we are in a war for our very survival, and I will not allow the antics of you and your kind to upset or interfere with our plans for this nation's defense. I have checked you out thoroughly in the past few days. We know you left Yale for lack of decent passing grades, not, as you have publicized, to fight for the oppressed. Furthermore, the FBI, the CIA, and the DIA recorded all your conversations with Castro, Arafat, Kim Jong-Il, Ghaddafi, Ortega, and many other known terrorists. If you make one attempt to disclose what we

97

have said in this meeting, or attempt to block passage of funding bills we need to secure our borders and protect this nation, I will have the charge of treason placed upon you, and you will be immediately incarcerated. Added charges will keep coming from the information that I have personal knowledge of, as well as further revelations of your treasonous activities."

He concluded, "Ms. Pelerine, I suggest you never attempt to threaten a standing President again, as your score card is much too easy to rip apart. I might add that even your former followers are scared to death to be associated with an enemy supporter, and they will quickly change sides if a publicized traitor is found in their midst. Once again, Ms. Pelerine, do you understand what I have just said, or do you need a trip to Bethesda as well?"

Pelerine had by now lost all of her bravado and posturing and sat like a little school girl being scolded for misbehaving. In a near whisper, she replied, "Yes, sir," and for the rest of the meeting, kept her lowered to her lap, or to the part of the table immediately in front of her.

At this point, the President looked around the table and noticed that General Carmine DeBona, the Chief of the US. Army Medical Research Institute of Infectious Diseases was standing and asking to be allowed to comment.

The President nodded and the General began. "Sir, we have been able to determine all the types of agents used and their sources. Moreover, as Dianne mentioned, we have the antibiotics and other medications in place to prevent the spread of the diseases. However, a new one has been found in Jacksonville, Florida, and this one appears quite serious, although we believe we will have it under control soon. The agent is Tuberculosis or TB to you old hands."

At this point, Barney yelled back, "General, have you gone loco, TB was cured long, long ago!" The General looked at Barney, ignored his outburst and looked back at the President, as he continued. "Sir, as I was saying, TB is about 95% contained in developing countries, but it still kills about 2 million a year. However, Russia has experienced a large increase in the past 10-14 years of a TB mutation that is a multi-drug resistant strain. Over a hundred years ago here in the U.S., one in five Americans got some form of sickness or another over TB-related bacillus, which are spread through breathing and thus are passed as airborne contaminants. We were able over many years to control this disease, because the antibiotics that we used actually worked."

"However, in the 1998 findings, we determined that 41% of the TB cases we were finding were coming from immigrants or travelers from overseas. The strains they bring are different from our own homegrown ones, and they tend to be very dangerous because while they enter the lungs, once they escape into the blood stream, they can infect every organ system, such as the brain, spine, and kidneys. Furthermore, it takes up to 6 weeks to incubate the culture of the TB bacteria, so it is often missed on X-rays and by then it may have entered the various vital organ sites."

"Sir, we now have over 217 suspected cases of TB in Jacksonville, but we don't have the equipment or medications for long-term care. That's because, once it's discovered to be the culprit, it requires four different types of antibiotics to combat it, and there's still a 50/50 chance of residual damage such as with eyesight, or a recurrence if not found soon enough. We can fight it, but it further complicates the efforts to combat the agents we are now fighting, and I thought this should be brought to everyone's attention." DeBona then looked directly at Barney, who appeared to be trying to crawl into his own chair, and for once looking embarrassed.

The next speaker, General Paxton, proceeded to inform them that all enemy submarines were locked on as targets, and concluded by saying, "Sir, at the first hint of any attempts to fire, they will be destroyed, as will the missiles from Iran or China. Further, if any missiles do manage to get through, then every one of their major cities and military targets will be destroyed with laser, radio wave, nuclear, and neutron weapons. Our weapons systems are ready and simply need your OK to end the threat."

The President, for once appearing Presidential, ended the meeting by saying, "I am in negotiations with the nations involved as well as with our allies, and I'm hoping for a major stand down by all parties, but if there are any further threats or attacks against the U.S., I will unhesitatingly unleash these new weapons against our enemies."

Chapter 9 – Hyder, Alaska

It was October 3rd, 22 days since the attacks had occurred in the three American cities, and the nation was slowly recovering. By now, the American leaders thought they had the situation reasonably well in hand, considering the loss of life and other casualties that had befallen those unfortunate cities.

America was still not ready to declare and initiate an all-out war without the approval of most of the friendly allied nations. President Warrington recalled what had befallen his predecessor, even with all such approvals. So in keeping with his past liberal Democrat convictions, he fell back on attempts to negotiate and appease the known enemy leaders.

Warrington's recent and newly-expressed hard line, which he had recently displayed at the secure Wyoming location at the beginning of the attacks, began to change as he flip-flopped from a more conservative view to a more moderate perspective, until it finally evolved into an even more accommodating and conciliatory viewpoint that an enemy's misjudgment had placed the entire world at further risk. He was now convinced that he must seek the path of peace, if only to protect future generations. The U.S. military remained eager to repay the terrorists and their supporting allies for the damage and casualties inflicted on American citizens, and the President agreed with the generals and admirals in private; but he wavered on taking immediate action, not only in his address to Congress, but also through the daily media bulletins.

The terrorists had been observing the American response since the September 11th attacks, even as they had been laying the groundwork for the next phases of attacks over the many months.

The town of Hyder, Alaska, consists of ramshackle shacks and stores and has neither municipal government, police force, nor a border-crossing checkpoint. In fact, Hyder is a small community of about 100 people at the southern end of Alaska, a mere two miles from the Canadian border town of Stewart. The Canadians, on the other hand, have a border checkpoint at Stewart along with official government representation; yet, it also remains another small border town, though with more than twice Hyder's population.

The Islamic and Chinese Special Forces terrorists had long ago determined that entering the U.S. through Hyder was ideal; without any border officials or even a policeman there, they could transport their goods from Canada to the U.S. with minimal chance of ever being stopped or caught. But to be sure, they had also provided themselves a good cover.

They had made frequent trips through Hyder from Canada to the U.S. in two older, beat-up pickup trucks. After a few days, they would return to Canada with slightly-spoiled fish that emitted a terrible smell. The Canadian authorities made jokes about them, since they seemed to be a strange group of men of Chinese and maybe Mexican heritage, and their going and returning with rods and reels of all sorts and types, as well as with crab and lobster traps and even tents and cots, was cause for amusement and jokes. All their equipment, passports, and drivers' licenses had been checked out by the Canadian

Border Officials on at least five or six occasions and seemed in proper order, although in reality most were forged. The Americans had never asked or bothered to check them out on their side when they passed through the town, and this odd group of people who purposely spoke various forms of broken English, had even attempted to sell or barter some of the more decent-smelling fish for tobacco products, fishing equipment, and even gasoline, though with rare success.

They experienced only one scare; when filling up once at a service station, one of the attendants familiar with the group had asked what the oxygen bottle was doing in the bed of the truck, as it looked quite out of place with all the other old and raggedy fishing equipment. One of the Chinese terrorists had answered in the sing song Cantonese fashion that it was for frish to bree, which cracked up the attendant and later became part of the humorous side of the oddball fishermen's lore.

The terrorists always tried to appear as uneducated Canadian immigrants who had somehow met and then teamed up to be fishermen of sorts. When asked, they said that their home town was another small town about four hours further inland from Stewart, which was not true, as they really lived in a motel about six hours away, but they said four just in case anybody got nosy. The Chinese men were in excellent physical shape, while the Mexicans (or whatever they were) were mostly overweight and older than their Chinese counterparts. But few people had noticed this, as the men were of little concern to citizens on either side of the border, or even to the Canadian border or law enforcement officials.

After establishing these patterns of behavior for several months with the locals, the terrorists were mostly ignored or forgotten by now ... except when someone attempted to mimic their accents or joke about their junky fishing equipment. Once they thought their cover was relatively secure, they then loaded the first of the radioactive bombs, which they transported in separate parts covered with plastic, and with smelly fish burlap sacks hiding them from view. They had then transported these over the border in the large coolers so often used for the fish and the bait.

Once inside the U.S., other terrorist cells had transported the oxygen bottles and those containing the WMD materials via the ferry or the rented fishing boats to Seattle, Washington, where they were trucked to the new target cities in rented U-haul trucks. Those drivers were instructed never to exceed the speed limits or do anything that might draw suspicion their way, as the Americans were now on full alert.

Although the Arab drivers used for this last leg of the journeys spoke English reasonably well, they were dressed as Mexicans from head to foot, even keeping an old sombrero and serape in the front seat to enhance their ethnic persona. They had practiced the Mexican accents and even carried Mexican driver's licenses and papers as new residents of the U.S. Each had a sensible cover story in case they were stopped, and had money to pay any traffic fines, if necessary. So, the drivers of the radioactive dirty bombs made their lonely, scary, and unique trips to their specific destinations unhampered and well within the timeframes established much earlier in the planning phases.

Most of the oxygen bottles were being transported over the border in a similar manner and had then taken to SCUBA diving boats, where the Chinese divers had racks of oxygen bottles on older boats owned by a Chinese businessman. Every one of the terrorists knew which ones contained the deadly agents. If the American crews asked about the bottles with the X marks, the divers would explain that they had leaky valves and were not to be used, as they would be replaced in Seattle after the dives.

All the practice dives were uneventful, and the small American crews while bored, were glad for the extra bit of income received from showing the owners' friends a good time. The Americans tried to be helpful and pleasant, but the Chinese divers seemed to want to be left alone, and they didn't drink, and so the Americans did all the drinking and played their favorite music, while the Chinese soldiers tried to appear like diving enthusiasts.

This system worked well until the next to last planned trip on October 3rd. After the dives were completed and late that same afternoon, one of the American crew members mentioned this odd diving group to his friendly bartender at his favorite Seattle watering hole. He had mentioned it several times before, but now he said that something just somehow seemed wrong with the whole picture. He observed to the bartender that the Chinese all seemed to be in great condition and swam like Navy SEALS, but they never asked to go to any new dive locations, or even seemed to much care that they were going to the same spots over and over again, and this was all in the last few months. He had gone diving with them a couple of times, but they seemed to be practicing descents and buddy breathing, like it was a training session instead of an enjoyable, relaxing outing. He noted that one seemed like the leader and was always there when new people appeared on the trips, then at times the same old people got cycled in again.

He was talking aloud, "Hell, they seem more like military people than us fun loving civilians." The bartender asked, "Do they always come here to Seattle and do they get checked by the port officials?" The crew man's answer was a boozy "Yeah, but they take the X'ed bottles into town, and return without them, and then they spend the night on the deck of the boat and we return to Alaska the next morning. I can't figure out why we come all the way here, if they're not going to visit the city or chase girls, I mean what kind of nut cases are these?"

The bartender, more astute and aware than his boozy friend, immediately called his policeman brother. His brother notified his department and the Coast Guard, who quickly developed a joint plan to follow this group to determine if they were terrorists or "merely" illegal immigrants. A story from a half-drunk crewman was not always the best way to gather intelligence or to legally trap these folks.

The next morning, October 4th, when the boat returned to Alaska as usual, it was followed both on radar and through visual observation from passing ships, with additional police and Coast Guard surveillance awaiting them in Alaska. Once in Alaska, the Chinese were not closely followed as would normally be the case, but instead were observed from rooftops and distant helicopters and bush planes to avoid detection. When their base of operations turned out to be a motel near the coastline, nobody went to question the motel owner or others in that location. It was strictly long-range observation and quite boring, as they observed the Chinese men run eight to ten miles every morning for the next five days. Though they never left together, they always met in a large vacant field, where they practiced martial arts and various other strange exercises.

The observers determined these were definitely military people, and this data went up the official U.S. and Canadian channels and chains of command. The question remained of what they were really up to. It took one more week, and one more diving trip request, for it to all come to a head.

Early on the morning of October 16th, two beat-up old trucks showed up at the coastline motel where those particular groups of Chinese were staying. Surprisingly, more Chinese-looking men arrived in other old trucks, along with some Mexicans or Middle Eastern-looking men. Since one group was out running and exercising, the new arrivals had to wait for their return. Some walked around the motel grounds, often in pairs. But the Chinese and the others seemed to have little to do with one another, unless they had to talk, or so it seemed. Next, the diving group arrived in ones and twos, as though they did not know one another, and then went to their rooms ignoring the truck people. About ten minutes later, their leader arrived alone and spoke to the leaders of the truck group. He pointed to his watch and went to his room. Five minutes later, all the Chinese from the motel went to their own rented SUVs, carrying wet suits, snorkels, masks, and flippers, and then backed them up to the old trucks. The old truck group started loading oxygen bottles into the back of the SUVs.

The Americans discussed the strategies of continuing to stalk the terrorists or taking them while they could, that is, in an open and relatively sparsely inhabited area. Here they could capture the majority of the group, but they knew there were others were in Seattle, and still others were over the Canadian border, because they obviously needed help and couldn't do everything the authorities believed they were up to with this few in numbers.

The Canadian authorities opted for continued surveillance, while the Americans determined that more harm would come to both nations if they waited. Besides, the cat would soon be out of the bag, since the Alaskan local police, the FBI, the Coast Guard, and the Seattle Police were tracking the recipients of the supposedly-damaged oxygen bottles. Meanwhile, the Royal Canadian Mounties were tracking the Canadian terrorist group via the trucks and the license plates, all of which had been photographed by the aerial surveillance team and then forwarded to the Canadian Vehicle Registry authorities.

The two groups agreed it wouldn't take long to find where the bottles were to be deposited in Seattle, as it would be difficult to disguise such awkward items without been seen. Likewise, the Canadian authorities believed it wouldn't take long to find their terrorists' – or illegals' – base camp, particularly after determining that only three roads led into the U.S. from this part of nearby Canada. It didn't take long to discover that the logical road that would cause the least trouble and suspicion would be the road through Stewart and Hyder.

A call to the border authorities in Stewart a few hours before arriving at the present surveillance location had revealed the story of the funny fishermen and their on-going fishing activities. Since they had passed through the town of Stewart often enough, it wouldn't be too difficult to locate where they'd been living, as it couldn't be too far away.

So the question still remained, take them now or later? The senior man present that day was an FBI agent, who then gave the order, without departmental approval, to take the suspected terrorists there and then.

In a matter of minutes, and about the time the last of the oxygen bottles was being loaded, helicopters from the FBI, the Alaskan National Guard, and the Coast Guard circled overhead, while over 40 American law enforcement officers accompanied by six Coast Guardsmen and four Mounties, circled the terrorists with guns at the ready.

The terrorists knew they had few weapons with them, the better to avoid detection, and knew resistance was futile–except for those wishing to die. The Arabs were in semi-shock and did not move when they heard the orders and saw the helicopters as well as the encircling law enforcement officers. The Chinese soldiers were given a command and they all ran and fell into a military line formation. At a second command, they all reached into their trouser watch pockets or their shirt pockets, pulled out and popped a pill into their mouths. This swift action occurred in a matter of seconds. The Arabs looked at the Chinese soldiers with a mixture of awe and amazement, as the stoic Chinese fell to the ground in their withering and obviously painful death throes.

Two of the Arabs nearest their own trucks and who had quickly pulled out hidden pistols were killed instantly, with one getting off two wild shots and the other never even getting to pull the trigger. It was later determined that one

Arab has sustained 62 bullets, while the other only had 49; upon later consideration, it was determined that only the good luck of them all shooting from the kneeling position had allowed the police and other officials to avoid shooting one another, in their amateurish semi-circle attack.

The live Arabs and the bodies of the dead were gathered up and flown to Seattle with two law enforcement officers sitting atop each living terrorist. In Seattle, the gloves came off and the laws and rules of warfare and civil law were set aside, just as the Geneva Convention Rules of Warfare had been set aside in WWII. It took two hours for the first Arab with broken arms and nose to start talking. The others lasted a bit longer, but by that night, they had all revealed what they heard or knew of the possible targeted cities. Unfortunately, none of them knew the actual detonation locations or who would set them off.

However, there was a delay in transmitting this information up the chain of command, primarily due to the senior intelligence analysts' uncertainty as to whether or not they were being been misled about the true targeted cities being planned for the next attacks. But by then it was too late anyway, as the plans were in motion and nothing could prevent the waiting disaster from occurring.

Chapter 10 – The Final War Room Meeting

18 October 2005 - Washington, D. C.

All the members of the Joint Chiefs of Staff stood before the President. The audience they had requested with him was granted on very short notice. The Chairman carried a paper in his hand, as did each of the other officers. The President had been expecting another update briefing and found it odd that all of the Joint Chiefs staff members were present together to submit an update, so he figured it must be quite important. But when he looked at the serious and drawn faces of the assembled officers, he immediately realized that this was not just another quick briefing, but a matter of very serious concern.

The President stood to shake hands, giving his usual fake smile, but the Chairman; General Paxton stated emphatically, "Sir, we are here to submit our letters of resignation!" Taken aback, Warrington sat down again, his synapses working at maximum speed while his mind attempted to digest and filter the startling new information. Looking up, he said, "General, what is all this about? And please be seated, I'm uncomfortable having you all stare down on me." None moved or appeared ready to move.

General Paxton stood straighter and said, "Mr. President, we are not here to debate you or even to justify our action. When you threw out the Vice President and then gave Barney and Susan hell, we thought maybe you'd finally seen for once that our enemies are serious, and that the road of continual negotiations and appeasement is the wrong and foolish path to take. Thus far, though, you've made some threats, but haven't taken any action. Jaw boning with our enemies has only given them more time to prepare their forces for an all-out assault on this nation. We can no longer provide the sure kill ratios to which we previously committed, because they're starting to displace their weapons systems, which makes it more difficult to insure we can kill all the submarines and missile and aircraft systems we had previously locked on."

"You have disregarded our best advice, which is from people who regard war as an anathema because we have all been there at different periods and in differing situations. We serve to protect this nation, and your weeks and weeks of procrastination and attempts at appeasement, have made our nation even more vulnerable to attacks that we may no longer be able to completely stop. You, sir, are a disgraceful coward in our most dire time of need, and you have jeopardized our population with your liberal, socialistic, stupidity. You may fire me if you wish, but I only ask that you accept the resignation letters of the other Joint Staff members and allow them to leave without further repercussions or retribution."

The stunned President then said, "Generals and Admiral Bennett, I appreciate your concerns and your feelings. I have been trying to find a way to avoid an all-out war on three or four fronts. If I did as you asked, we would have an all-out war with not only China, Iran, and the overseas terrorist elements, but those internal terrorists, too. Before we go on—and I promise you I will in the end accept your resignations—I can only hope that you will reconsider your decision. My question to you now, General Paxton, is this: is everyone here in complete agreement with your decision and views? Because if that is the case, I would at least appreciate the courtesy of hearing anyone out on their different point of view."

Paxton thought for a moment, and then said, "Mr. President, General Guy, the Commandant of the Marine Corps, does not totally agree with everything; he went along to insure we were able to present a united front and consensus."

The President nodded towards General Guy and then asked him to please explain why he differed from the others. General Guy stepped forward to the edge of the Oval Office desk, and began.

"Mr. President, I want you to know here and now that I still stand by my fellow Joint Staff members, and my main concern is the same as yours. I believe a four- or five-front war would prove disastrous even if we ultimately win in the end; that is, it could be a Pyrrhic victory. You'll recall this term was made famous by King Pyrrhus of Epirus when he defeated the Romans, but had few of his own army still left standing."

"My view is that we keep all the options in mind, but rather than attack all the enemy forces at once which would ensure their immediate retaliation, we do it more incrementally to avoid war on too many fronts. Instead, I suggest we immediately destroy all the Iranian subs wherever they're found–and there are only three to destroy. At the same time we should destroy all Chinese subs in the Caribbean, as well as any other subs from any country that appear to threaten our nation or our armed forces."

"If this plan is to work correctly, we also must destroy Iran completely and without concern for their population, or we will suffer greatly. We will then get immediate cooperation from others, such as we saw with Libya a while ago and also with the Russians after they were clobbered by terrorist actions ... especially if we take out Iran and then threaten complete annihilation of every other country who has been supporting our enemies–including the Latin American countries that we know are supporting the terrorists' campaign—as we will have just demonstrated our resolve with the destruction of Iran."

"We must also send a blunt and world-wide message to demonstrate that those providing financial support of terrorists or terrorist organizations, will be hunted down and killed by our Special Forces or Intelligence Operatives. This method dries up the funding and support for the terrorists, and they'll pull back. China, in the meantime, will remain in a quandary, as they'll know we are on to them and have destroyed a number of their subs, but we have obviously allowed others to escape. Thus, they will have to declare war on us; or hopefully after seeing what happened to Iran, they will not make a move that is guaranteed to destroy their own nation."

"The only other alternative that I can see is the one submitted to you by General Paxton earlier. However, my suggestion is not to hit them all at once and thereby unite them, but rather to divide them and take them out piecemeal, should they continue to seek war with us. That, Sir, is the gist of my recommendations."

The President eyed the Commandant and thought to himself, I always knew those dammed Marines were crazy and cocky, but he has proven to be smarter than all the rest on this global issue.

Warrington no longer had a VP, and was now about to lose his senior military leaders as well, that is, if he could not somehow find a solution or compromise quickly. He considered for a moment on how to respond, and then said, "Gentlemen, as I've said, I have tried to avoid an all-fronts war; negotiations and discussions have thus far proven fruitless, and it is also true that in my attempts to mediate a peaceful resolution, I have unfortunately allowed the enemy to become better prepared. This occurred on my watch and while I have desperately tried to avoid a world-wide, all-fronts war, because I also understand the inevitable consequences that are certain to follow."

He continued, "I believe that General Guy has provided the most sensible and responsible approach to this situation that I have yet heard. If you gentlemen will agree to General Guy's plan, I am prepared to issue the directives and authorizations you seek. But I beg you not to leave at this juncture, as I can't do this alone. I ask that you remain at your posts: not for my sake, as history will surely now judge me harshly, but rather for the sake of our nation and our people." The Generals and the sole Admiral were shocked and somewhat remorseful to see the tears unashamedly running down the President's cheeks. They each looked down at their shoes for a moment or two, trying their best to avoid their President's unmanly, desperate display of emotion. After a moment of thought, reflection, and silence, Admiral Bennett stood up straighter and stated that he, for one, agreed with and would support the Jarhead's plan.

This provoked a smile on the formerly serious faces of the other Joint Chiefs members, who also stood straighter one by one and agreed to Commandant Guy's plan for the upcoming war. In fact, within a minute or two they all stood shaking hands, patting one another as well as the President on the back, and misty eyes on all their faces. So simply asking who had other suggestions had averted yet another major crisis.

Just as they were preparing to leave the Oval Office, Ralph Cutting, the President's Chief of Staff, entered the room unannounced and said, "Mr. President, Los Angeles and Chicago have been attacked with what we think are radioactive bombs, and maybe other WMD agents."

Everyone in the room was still looking at each other in stunned silence, when, seconds later, Press Secretary Erika Schultz entered the room in tears, whispering that New York City had also just been attacked with a radioactive bomb.

Chapter 11 – The Chicago, New York City and Los Angeles Terrorists

18 October 2005

The main terrorist networks were dwindling in size, but most of their members were unaware of this, since news censorship was now in full force. Government agents were now at the editorial offices of each television news station and newspaper, reviewing the planned content of their broadcasts and newspapers to insure the enemy did not receive unintended intelligence. Even Republicans were griping about excessive government intrusions on the freedom of the press and media–that is, until the attacks in the three large cities happened.

The terrorists had planned well for the three larger American cities: the bombs went off almost all on schedule, and the pest control trucks in Los Angeles and New York City had sent the mists of VX gas across portions of the two cities, some 30 minutes before the bombs went off. Meanwhile, other well-placed terrorists attempted to introduce the biological agents, which had been brought in welded parts of the few remaining oxygen and propane bottles, and had also reached their destinations on schedule. The terrorists attempted to place them into the fire stations, the hospitals and clinics. But with the nation now on full alert, almost all were captured or shot before they could unleash the deadly agents.

However, two individuals in LA and one in NYC were able to place the biological agents in large stores and in a library instead of their planned targets. They opened the packages, set the biological agents near the ventilation systems, and simply waited for the half hour to pass when the bombs were to be set off. Nobody noticed what they had done, though some may have wondered why these men were so happy and smiling at everyone. Everything occurred as intended in the planned LA and NYC attacks.

But in Chicago, the oxygen bottles with the VX gas were placed alongside a pest control truck that had blown an engine gasket, so everything was being temporarily stored in an Arab-American auto repair shop. There, a customer's 11-year old son became bored while his dad awaited the mechanic's evaluation of the needed repairs. He noticed the oxygen bottles, saw the twist handles on the top of the seven lined-up bottles and decided to test the air that was supposed to come out. Instead, he got a good whiff of VX gas and died instantly. His father and the mechanic did not notice the boy until a few moments later, and as they approached the fallen boy, they also received a whiff of the gas. They could hear the hissing sound coming from the bottle, and the father tried to turn off the valve, but he turned it the wrong way and he also fell over dead. Even though the mechanic knew the tanks' contents and had lain flat on his back on the floor at the first smell of the gas, he could do nothing and only lasted 20 seconds longer.

Although the VX nerve gas had merely seeped out of the one oxygen cylinder, the winds had carried the gases to neighboring buildings and apartments. Soon, the effects of this toxic and lethal gas were being felt by people in that neighborhood. Some felt their vision blurring and began to panic; others noted that their bodily control functions were becoming impaired. All this caused a massive influx of phone calls to the police and fire departments, as well as to the various ambulance services. Of course, people were affected differently, as infants, young children and the old succumbed more quickly because their bodies were unable to fight the toxicity of the nerve gases. Younger, healthier adults were affected by symptoms of various sorts, but none that were completely incapacitating.

The wind had carried most of the gases into the bright sunlight, and the sun's action dissipated some of their toxicity, while still other airborne particles attracted the gas molecules that stuck to them, thus taking some portions of the toxic gases far away and into the air currents.

Police and fire watch commanders, realizing that the flood of emergency phone calls meant a mass evacuation of the surrounding area might be required, sent police and fire units to cordon off a five-block area around the location from where most of the calls had originated. Those responders sent to the cordoned area were told to don their protective nuclear, biological, and chemical gear, but few had them in their vehicles or had the right sizes if they were available, and so most chose not to don the gear. Besides, some responders thought that seeing them like that could frighten the citizens even more, so they stood their ground unprotected.

It took the Hazmat teams sent into the center of the neighborhood in question some 20 minutes to locate the gas source and then to finally shut off the cylinder valve. But a number of the unprotected policemen and medics from the ambulance crews who had followed the Hazmat teams into the infected neighborhood, were soon feeling the effects of even small doses of the VX gases, and began dying as they neared the auto repair shop.

The Chicago Terrorist

Abdula Mattar, a Jordanian terrorist, had said his final prayers to Allah, and now thought dreamily of the beautiful place he would soon be seeing for himself. He had rented a fifth floor apartment in downtown Chicago, figuring that a higher airburst would spread the radioactive material even further away from the blast center than if it detonated at ground level. As a warrior of Islam, he had been promised that his family would be well cared for after he became a hero of Islam for his courageous and suicidal deed. The thought of the 72 beautiful women who would soon be available to him–his Islamic view of Heaven–caused him to smile in anticipation as he slowly pushed the little red button, that then sent the electrical charge which would set off the radioactive bomb that would destroy so many, many infidels. His last thought before he was blown into oblivion was not of his family or even of the Koran, but of the wonderful legacy he would leave to the American history books, that is, once America became a Muslim nation.

After the blast, the strong winds circling the city continued to deposit the deadly radioactive agents on the population. Tallies of massive casualties would have to be counted, and the survivors cared for on a massive scale, a circumstance that had not been anticipated by the authorities or emergency and disaster planners, and therefore had not been fully funded.

The New York City Terrorist

In New York City, Sofwan Koheggi from Kuwait was beginning to question his own religious beliefs and the need to kill so many innocent people. But he also had realized that were he not to accomplish his assignment, his family would be brutalized and killed in extremely painful ways. He knew this because he had killed people in that manner himself. That he would be regarded and revered as a martyr and hero of Islam was not something he truly wished to achieve.

His terrorist activities used to give him an adrenaline rush, and he had prayed, like others, to not be criticized. But he had been looking through a Christian Bible for several years, initially to find the errors of the Christian beliefs, and then to try to understand why they could not accept Mohammed as the last Prophet and Islam and as the giver of the true and last words of Allah (God). As a non-practicing doctor of medicine and certified electrical engineer, his inquiring mind was never one to remain dormant and simply follow all religious pronouncements as Koranic gospel.

He was also a part-time student of history and archeology, who sometimes found he was wondering about the recent discoveries in the Holy Land and some of which sometimes seemed to support the Christian's or Jewish beliefs. Could there really be more to Christianity and Judaism than he had been led to understand?

At an earlier period of his life, Koheggi had found historical documentation regarding the unbelievably decadent and sick behavior of early Christian church leaders. He had read of the long-ago Popes who had led lives of debauchery and drunkenness, and of the Church of England and other Protestant denominations, whose leaders had also committed equally despicable acts and even cruelly dispatched those who defied their views. And while he knew and understood those facts, he also acknowledged that today's Christians were more aligned with what was originally conceived by the Prophet Jesus. Furthermore, he knew there was no possible way out for him or the others like him, as once you joined the terrorist bands and cells, the only way out was suicide or allowing them to torture you to death unless you could find a place to hide, but then your family would pay the price.

Because of his mental turmoil, Sofwan had been to late to rent an apartment high enough to obtain maximum dispersion of the radioactive dirty bomb elements. Now it was too late to move to a top floor apartment and then try to move the weapon up there without being noticed. After all, he did look very much the Middle East Arab even in his western attire, so moving anything besides the normal items, of which he had few, would be bound to attract attention and the possibility of the authorities then being notified loomed as a real possibility.

The weapon had been delivered right to his hotel room in the west side of NYC, so to prevent further opportunities for unwanted discovery; he decided to set the bomb off in his hotel room.

As the time neared for detonation, Sofwan contemplated his life and thought what a shame it was going to be to lose the keen mind and the skills that he had acquired as a doctor and an engineer. Perhaps he might never have joined the terrorist cell had he been older and a bit wiser at the time, but that no longer mattered, as it would all end in a flash. As he placed his finger over the red button and while awaiting the scheduled time, he did something very strange: he said the Christian Lord's Prayer very quietly and slowly from memory of the Bible, and then asked for the Christian God's and the Islamic Allah's forgiveness for what he was about to do. He wept softly, knowing that he would be responsible for the thousands who would die with him. He took a deep breath as though preparing to dive underwater, and then pressed the button.

But what Sofwan had not taken into consideration was that the tall buildings in NYC would block much of the blast and the fallout, thus limiting the amount of damage and casualties than would otherwise be expected. But that was not really his concern, as enough would die to prove that his mission had been accomplished.

The Los Angeles Terrorist

In Los Angeles, the scenario played out quite differently. The terrorists were supposed to transport the bomb to an area near City Hall. However, in their eagerness to get there on time, a cop caught them speeding about 10 miles per hour over the posted speed limit and began a pursuit to make his ticket quota. The terrorists thought they had been identified and sped up to lose their pursuer. However, the cop called other police units and the chase went on for nearly 35 minutes. Unbeknownst to the terrorists, firing their handguns at the pursuing police cars simply served to bring more law enforcement units to the scene, and causing the expanding chase to move the terrorists' car farther away from the city center. They were terrified that they might fail in their mission, as they were already anticipating their own deaths with the bomb's detonation and failure would bring shame on their own honor and their family's name.

Eventually, the terrorists' car was cornered from both ends on a freeway up ramp. They knew their time was up, so they assembled the one part needed to set off the bomb, then wired and prepared the bomb for detonation.

Meanwhile, the police remained some distance away from the armed terrorists' car waiting for the SWAT Team. Knowing they were 20 minutes ahead of schedule and agreeing that they had no choice, the terrorists began to loudly chant, "Allah Akbar, Allah Akbar" (God is great, God is great), as though it would matter to the police.

Their license plate number had been transmitted to all law enforcement agencies nationwide, and the actual chase was being televised from a local news helicopter, hardly an unusual occurrence in Los Angeles. When the TV footage was analyzed later, everyone could see the initial explosion taking the roof off the terrorists' car and then building into a large cloud of radioactive fallout. The news helicopter was destroyed with such force that only quarter-sized pieces were found of the craft, and none of the occupants' body parts was ever found. There also wasn't much left of the police cars or the officers who had reached the ramp location; some were later identified only by the identification numbers on the roofs of the cars. But that mattered little in the overall picture as many, many, were killed, and many more would soon die of the radioactive material in the air. By a strange twist of fate, a Santa Anna wind was blowing through the LA basin that day and the hot winds went from east to west rather than in the usual, opposite direction. Thus, the radioactive fallout and much of the VX gas released from the oxygen bottles blew out to sea rather than inland, as intended.

While the three cities were not destroyed, as they would have been by a nuclear missile attack, they would still be out of commission as centers for commerce for a long and as yet undetermined period of time, and the monetary costs could run in the trillions. With all the horrific destruction and the very heavy loss of life, the entire American population was left to wonder: what were their President and military doing, why they had not prevented this from happening, and what other cities might be the next targets?

Worse yet, due to bits of information leaked from various government sources, it did not take long for the general public to learn of the Chinese and Arab involvement in the Tijuana, Mexico and San Diego smallpox epidemic. As panic and fear set in, gangs began to form and organize to confront people of Chinese and Arab descent, and with consequences that were bound to be very frightful to these and other ethnic groups.

Chapter 12 – America Responds

18 October 2005

Cheyenne Mountain, Wyoming

The conversations in the Oval Office had abruptly ended upon learning of the nuclear blasts in the three large cities of New York, Los Angeles, and Chicago. Washington, D.C., was then considered the next most-likely target and the government's crisis plan called for getting the President and his Administration away from that location as soon as possible.

So once again, the Secret Service quickly flew the President, his entire Cabinet, various other government agency heads and leaders, and the entire membership of the Joint Chiefs of Staff to the emergency underground Command Post located in the mountains of Wyoming, the same site of a previous emergency meeting just over a month ago.

After the WMD attack notification, President Warrington had tried to come up with a saying or statement that would have some historical significance for posterity. But his anguish, shock, and temporary personal fears rendered him able only to mumble a statement from a long ago book.

Turning to General Guy, he had said in a low and almost trembling voice, "Let loose the dogs of war," forgetting that his order should have been given to the Chairman of the Joint Chiefs of Staff, not to the Marine

Corps Commandant. However, that protocol violation was overlooked without comment as they each tried to sort out their own thoughts and feelings.

It only took another moment for the Head of the Secret Service to begin pushing everyone to waiting helicopters for the short flight to Air Force One, already turning up its engines on the nearby Andrews Air Force Base tarmac. Before leaving, the President signed the official papers instructing the military to commence military combat operations.

The only real question under discussion now was whether or not to take out Syria as well. The conclusion reached was to wait and see the results of the U.S. military's new weapons accuracy, and how the Syrians reacted to Iran's destruction. The orders were sent to U.S. military organizations, and now as they flew to Wyoming, they could only wait to hear the results.

Upon their arrival at the underground location four plus hours later, the President, his Chief of Staff, his security detail, and the Joint Chiefs staff went directly to the War Room. Satellites were now focusing directly on the targets, which could be seen on the seemingly-endless computer and TV screens surrounding the walls of the War Room.

A 3-star Navy Admiral approached the President's group and said, "Sir, you will probably not see the destruction of the submarines, as they are being hit by radio waves of such force that everyone inside them will be dead in seconds, so there will be no visible large explosions. However, the satellites' laser rays will appear in red, so you'll be able to see missiles destructing on their launch pads or in the air if they're able to get one off."

He continued, "At this point, Sir, we've killed off all of the Iranian subs, and all but two of the Chinese subs that were headed out to sea, and which you had previously authorized us to destroy. Those two know something has happened, but they haven't moved very far yet, and we've picked up confused calls from the subs to the mainland requesting instructions, as they've lost contact with the ones we destroyed."

The President paled again and said almost to himself, "My God in Heaven, I have actually released the dogs of war, God help us." Everyone in the very large room could see on the various wall monitors numerous Iranian soldiers running for the missile launch pads, having just finished with their prayers.

The President seemed to say a silent prayer himself as the first of the missile sites in Iran blew up on its launch pad, the tell-tale red laser ray remaining on target for a minute even after the missile had already blown up. Three screens away, another monitor showed three missiles take off, with two actually leaving the launch pads, while the third blew up in place.

As the two airborne missiles climbed, the Iranian civilians were all cheering with fists raised on high and with a sickening glee of both hatred and happiness on their faces, while others were twirling in uncontrollable dances of excitement. Many were pointing at the rising missiles, but when first one, and then nanoseconds later the second missile exploded in flight, the people on the ground stopped dancing and then watched with disappointment and fascination as the missile pieces began falling back to earth.

During the events of the last weeks and months, the United Nations had been for all practical purposes ignored by the great powers. Now they seemed nothing more than a squabbling group of corrupt and ineffectual members, sending forth condemnations and mighty-sounding words that threatened future UN actions. As they realized that none of the key nations were paying attention to them, they finally began to recognize that they were going to become nothing more than another League of Nations, that is, a corrupt paper tiger lacking the teeth to do what they professed to be able do.

The U.S., in fact, had already begun the process of forming a new group of nations, who agreed for starters to promote freedom of the press, freedom of religion, and freedom of speech—or they could not join this new club. Thus, any nation with a dictatorship, theocracy, communistic or even an extremely socialistic government would not be invited to join the new group.

The headquarters location for this new group of nations would be on the island of Bermuda, in order to avoid the disastrous behavior of past UN representatives in the United States. In fact, the representatives of this fledgling organization would no longer receive diplomatic immunity and would no longer be able to live on large UN-provided pensions. Instead, they would receive only what their own governments chose to provide to their representatives. It became clear that the time for excessive UN handouts to diplomats was over, and diplomats had begun leaving NYC in droves as they realized that soon the money would stop flowing, and their high-living ways would soon come to an abrupt end.

Iran and China

Both the Iranian and Chinese militaries had been unsure exactly how the U.S. would react after the bombing of its three major cities, but they had expected some form of retaliation and were therefore on alert. As soon as they lost contact with their respective subs, both countries' military leadership knew retaliation was underway, since they could hardly hide their participation and collusion with the terrorists who had in turn attacked the American homeland.

Iran

On October 18th, the crowds of civilians standing around the gun and missile positions had gone into a frenzy of joy and laughter when they heard the news of the nuclear bombing of the U.S. on their radios, yelling "Allah Akbar, Allah, Akbar," as the nations missiles remained pointed towards Israel and the despised American fleet in the Arabian Gulf. Now, though, even the poorest and least-educated Iranian peasant knew that the winds of war were certain to come their way, and very soon.

Normally, the fire from the explosions would have incinerated the biological and chemical agents placed inside the warheads, which should have also blown up. Instead, the missile warheads ejected away from the missile bodies and landed in the midst of the Iranian crowds, where they then blew up in a controlled manner so as not to destroy the toxic gases or kill the destructive disease agents. The horrified Iranian crowds watched as small plumes of gases and biological agents descended upon them, sometimes in droplet form and other times in a gas form. Realizing what had occurred; some started praying, while others ran in panic and terror.

As missile after missile was destroyed either in flight or on its pad, the Iranian countryside and cities became littered with dead humans, animals, plants, and even small insects, which like the birds, fell out of the sky in large numbers.

The major cities of Iran had all kept missile sites in open buildings, on school grounds, and even around hospitals, all the while expecting to be bombed with conventional ordnance that would justify them condemning the United States Government for specifically targeting civilians. But the gloves of propriety and gentlemanly rules had been set aside, and the nations who had attacked the United States of America were now feeling the wrath of a nation no longer constrained by the UN, or the laws of civil jurisprudence. Instead, they were encountering an uncompromising nation that would now brook no excuses, nor accept any attempts to negotiate from all enemy nations. The kindly sleeping giant had finally reawakened, and there would be hell to pay for all who had harmed it, both now as well as in the past.

Iran soon became a nation of the dying and the dead; and while many people survived, for many generations to come they would hesitate ever to suggest warfare or even threaten other nations or peoples to promote their own agendas. Instead, the survivors would return to their tribal roots and argue over who had really been responsible for this slaughter of millions of their countrymen.

Many of the less-educated citizens expected the Christians to come and subjugate them, and then sell them into slavery as the Koran had taught them. They expected eventually to be forced to join the Christian religion or be killed. They would sit and discuss the events they were certain would come, their thoughts ranging from anger to sadness, and then to fear. Their only real hope was in knowing that Christians were supposed to be weak rulers, and perhaps would give them some hope for their families if they fully cooperated.

In fact, many were beginning for the first time to question both the Koran itself and their own religious leaders, who had brought such terrible destruction and suffering upon their nation. As they thought about the future, they remembered that Christians might be more decadent and less religious than Muslims, but they also had a strange concept of forgiveness and helping their former enemies, as demonstrated by how they had treated Japan and Germany over some 60 years ago.

Many Muslims began to think that maybe there was something to the Christian beliefs after all, and many decided to learn more about this foreign religion that might well be the salvation of their families, and possibly someday, of their destroyed nation as well.

Mobs of their own countrymen and women began to hunt down, stone to death or hang–in their villages, towns, or city squares–those Iranian religious leaders who still spewed the venom of hatred and anti-western propaganda. Eventually, Islam would begin to fall apart in Iran, and this would start to catch on in other Islamic nations, which feared that destruction similar to Iran's would befall their own nations and people. They all knew that the retaliation they had suffered was the result of their own leaders' support of terrorists and the hatred preached toward the West and Israel, and which had been taught and promoted by their own Islamic religious leaders. The talk in the streets of those other Middle Eastern Islamic nations turned to making peace with Israel and also to assisting the U.S. to hunt down the terrorist organizations and cells.

This turnabout was the result of several factors: fear, a fatalistic concept within their own religion, and a desire to end all the fighting. They might lose some pride in the end, but the alternatives seemed suicidal for all if they did not change their ways and their beliefs.

But all this would take much time and would not happen overnight. Someday in the near future, the countryside and cities of all Islamic nations would have Christian churches and even Jewish Synagogues, along with Buddhist and Hindu places of worship available to all. But that was way in the future, since for now the Islamic religion was still based on a belief that the government and religion were one and the same. Giving away their power was still, for many, too much for them to accept an so they would continue to fight for their religious beliefs.

Even India was in for great upheavals with regard to future religious changes and acceptance of others, as the Muslim population in India nearly exceeded that of the entire U.S. population.

Change to the Muslim nations would eventually come, perhaps not as quickly as some wanted, but the threat of the destruction hung heavy over any nation that chose to defy and oppose the U.S. with arms. They knew the U.S. could and would destroy them in short order, and that threat alone would be the cause of more rapid progress, towards more open and less threatening Islamic societies.

China

The Chinese Government and military, on the other hand, now realized that it had badly miscalculated not only the United States' resolve, but that of the other Western nations which were now quickly uniting into a more powerful military and economic force. Their decision to assist each other had not been taken into China's planning for their war considerations. So, instead of the U.S. being surrounded by enemy nations and groups, it was China that stood out alone as the leader of this attempt to destroy the U.S.

The Chinese Government was in daily contact with the U.S., desperately trying to find a way out of its dilemma after it realized too late, that the new weapons systems used by the U.S. on Iran could also quickly defeat their entire WMD inventories, missile units, sub fleets, and air forces. The old leaders of the Chinese Communist Party were aware of the change of party member attitudes during their regular legislative meetings, as many formerly quiet and seemingly subservient representatives were becoming more vocal opponents of both past and present policies. Most representatives had heard the news and realized that China had much to do with the failure to destroy America, along with their obvious assistance to the various terrorist groups.

Questions were now being asked about the disappearance of a large number of submarines and their crews, as the family members began demanding information from their representatives. Worse yet, speeches by the U.S. President regarding China's leadership and their promotion of this disastrous venture had placed China onto a war footing with the US.

The Chinese people were becoming alarmed at the possible consequences of their leaders' insane actions, and they wanted no part of the Iranians' fate. Thus, the small rebellions that began to break out around the countryside grew in intensity, as some of the smaller and more distant units of the People's Army joined the rebels.

On October 19th - they were a day ahead of the West – the Chinese leadership met in closed session with representatives from the military and key members of the legislature to discuss these new and unsettling events. Following the standard practice of all good Communists, the Communist Party leadership and the military leaders from all branches strode up one by one to the podium to declare their failures and their sorrow for being unsuccessful. They all agreed to submit their resignations immediately, if so desired by the assembled group.

After the last leader spoke, the Party Chairman stated again that anyone wishing to accept or dispute any of the offered resignations should speak up. Among the delegates and representatives were two younger American business-trained representatives, which was unusual because of their relative youth (late 40s). Their brilliant academic achievements, both in China and in the United States, had put them in the forefront of setting up free enterprise business enclaves within China. These had proved to be successful and had provided much-needed funding to the antiquated and cash-strapped Chinese Communist government.

The more vocal of the two was Lai Ming Qian, and his friend and co-worker, Mao Tse Zhou. Comrade Qian stood up slowly and a bit fearfully, knowing he was breeching an unspoken protocol. Looking directly at the Chairman of the entire Chinese Communist Party, he began to speak in a quavering voice. He uttered the following words: "Comrade Chairman, and honored leaders. I, like most others here, have heard and read the reports of our nation's involvement in the attacks on America, through the foreign media and through our own sources here within the Party.

We are about to become engaged in a war where we have small chance of success against the new weapons used by the Americans on Iran, and we also understand that part of our submarine fleet is missing and presumed sunk or destroyed in the same way the American destroyed those of the Iranian government. Further, we understand that our missiles are about to be destroyed through some satellite weapon, just as the Americans destroyed those of Iran."

"More importantly, we are likely to receive retribution from the Americans for the loss of their people and cities, such as the world have never known before. Their casualties were enormous from the use of radioactive bombs supplied by our government, as well as by the chemical and biological agents used by the terrorists, whom, I might add, we encouraged, led, and assisted in this disastrous and foolhardy enterprise."

"In short, we have already lost and will soon feel the awesome power of nuclear weapons and who knows what else, and our casualties will most likely be the end of China as a nation. In my opinion, we have only one remote chance of preventing this from occurring, and that is through a complete change of our government's leadership, and to change from being a Communist government to that of a democratic and free enterprise system for the entire nation, rather than just in the enclaves we have already established. Additionally, those responsible for this unbelievable disaster to our nation must be tried and dispatched immediately."

Qian's voice had become increasingly strong as he spoke, and a new tone of confidence and authority could be heard in it. He continued, "Comrades, in my opinion, the only way we can save our nation and our people is through previously unheard of and extraordinary actions. Therefore, I humbly request that a vote be taken by the National People's Congress to accept the resignation offers of the Chairman and the entire Central Committee Leaders, now! A new government must be formed that is democratic, religiously open, and free market in nature and it must be installed as quickly as possible to prevent a catastrophic end to our nation and our people. With your permission, Comrade Chairman, I will now ask for a vote for or against this proposal. I ask everyone here to please stand if you agree to my recommendation."

The Chairman, somewhat bewildered by this enormous turn of events, slowly nodded, although some there were unsure if he nodded for the vote to be taken, or if he was simply nodding in disbelief and bewilderment. In any case, they proceeded, and approximately 68% of the National People's Congress stood, and then all waited in astonishment about what to do next.

"Comrade Chairman," said Qian, "The vote has been taken and your resignations are now approved. Next we must select a new leader to form the new government. Do we have any nominations from the floor?"

Qian's friend Zhou spoke up and shouted, "I nominate Comrade Lai Ming Qian to be the head of the new government. All who agree please stand so we may count the votes." But Qian whispered, ""No, Zhou, we must have a second on the nomination, and besides, you are much better qualified for this awesome responsibility than I." Zhou then turned to the National People's Congress and shouted, "Is there a second on my nomination?" To everyone's surprise, an old Navy Admiral, who had long ago fallen into disfavor with the Party leaders even though his military career had been more than exemplary, stood up and then seconded the nomination for Chairman.

The assembly broke into pandemonium as some began heated discussions with their fellow Congressmen and women, with many still unsure of what had just happened while still others were unable to comprehend the enormity of their actions or inactions. They knew that those who supported Qian were sure to get good future government positions and rewards, while those who opposed him would incur the opposite fate. Many were pushing up towards Qian to express their congratulations on him being chosen as the first democratically-elected leader of the new government, although many did not fully understand what that meant or even how it would operate.

Among the crowd of milling people was an old General who finally got in front of the smiling, newly-elected leader. The old General shouted, "My father and mother were part of Mao's long march, and we have lived by the Communist Party all our lives, and now I may die for the Party, but you will not take all we have worked for away from us, you American turncoat!" And with that, he drew his pistol and fired four bullets into Qian before the old General could be stopped and taken away by guards.

The Chairman and the Central Committee members observed all this and walked silently out of the meeting to adjourn to a nearby conference room. Zhou, now in tears because Qian was clearly dead, turned to the frightened and noisy crowd and yelled above the din, "Please, please do not leave. This is what we can expect from the Chairman and the Central Committee, and for now I ask for a vote to hold them in custody.

All now please raise your hands high if you agree." The crowd now managed an almost 80% show of raised hands while the vote was counted by orderlies. That done, Zhou ordered the military guards to round up the Central Committee members and keep them under house arrest. The senior guard officer was unsure of Zhou's authority, and the old Admiral once again came to the rescue and nodded at the guards to carry out the orders. Then the Admiral shouted, "We must now take another vote for the leader of our new government, and I nominate Mao Tse Zhou for the office of our new leader."

Zhou, still recovering from seeing his friend being shot before his very eyes, and covered with blood and tissue splatter from the wounds, simply stood with tears running down his cheeks as he watched his fellow Congressional representatives vote him into office, with an overwhelming majority of all but five voting. They spent the rest of the meeting time selecting other moderates or even non-Party members to the major positions of authority, and the Admiral now held the highest military position.

Zhou informed those gathered there that he would now call the President of the United States and do whatever was needed to prevent a war between the two nations. Everyone clapped in agreement, and Zhou headed off with the old

Admiral to call the Americans to beg forgiveness and inform them of the recent change in government. Zhou was unsure if he was up to the task, or if he was even worthy of talking to someone so high in a foreign government, for it was not he but Qian who had had the guts and nerve to face the Communist Party Chairman.

While he had supported Qian in theory, he was not the one who had promoted this concept. But the old Admiral, sensing Zhou's youth and fears, guided him to the Chairman's seat of authority, gave some orders to the startled assistant, and had the call placed to the U.S. President's office. What was to be said in this conversation could either save the country, send them into oblivion, or end in a surrender of China to the United States.

The Admiral expressed his views to Zhou on what to say from his experiences with U.S. officials, but in the end it would be Zhou's new-found leadership role and his ability to negotiate, that would either save or destroy his nation.

Chapter 13 – The U.S. and Chinese Dilemmas

18 October 2005

The Chinese Phone Call

On the evening of October 18th (October 19th in China), President Warrington was informed of the urgent call from China's new leader. This was most strange, because ever since the Communists took over in 1949, the Chinese leader had always been called the Chairman. It was also an unexpected and awkward situation, since the U.S. was in the final planning and preparation stages to destroy all the military bases and missile sites from which the Chinese could launch a first strike, after which the U.S. would systematically destroy the rest of China's key military targets. The plan was to then move on to the Chinese communications and infrastructure targets that appeared on the U.S. military's computer screens. This would all be accomplished before targeting China's major cities with their teeming populations.

The USAF nuclear bombs were already loaded onto aircraft and ready to leave their bases for their selected targets, while American submarines were testing their nuclear checklists one last time before launching their missiles. The nuclear ground missiles were being also being re-targeted and readjusted based on the latest satellite photos and target acquisitions, to ensure double or triple strikes on the major cities and installations. The thinking was that hitting those most capable of launching a first

141

round nuclear strike would prevent the Chinese from striking back at the U.S. Thus, the Chinese phone call came at a most inopportune time, and yet, it might just save millions upon millions of innocent lives were the Chinese to decide to surrender unconditionally.

A quickly-aging President Warrington took the phone call from the Chinese leader after gathering his Chief of Staff, Press Secretary, CIA and FBI liaison officers with him, for he wanted witnesses to this most important phone call. He flipped on the speaker phone and recording switches so that, for political as well as historical purposes, all in the Oval Office could hear the recorded conversation.

Mao Tse Zhou spoke perfect English, but initially with a fear and hesitancy in his voice that caused him to sound like a young boy whose voice was changing. This was obviously due to talking to the most powerful man in the world. For his part, Zhou realized that he was speaking for the Chinese people, knowing that soon he would be begging for their lives to be spared, even if his own must eventually be forfeit.

So Zhou began his dreaded phone call. "Mr. President, Sir. I know we have but little time before your nation attacks mine, and you would be completely justified in doing so. I am calling to tell you that, during the last hour and 10 minutes, we have held a meeting of the People's National Congress along with the Chairman and members of the Central Committee. My friend Mr. Qian spoke of the shameful and disgraceful attacks on American cities by our Party leadership and of their support of the terrorist organizations that were responsible for the actual attacks. As you probably know, the radioactive bombs used on Los

Angeles, Chicago, and New York City were manufactured in China and supplied to the Islamic terrorists, who in turn did their evil deeds."

Zhou continued, "Sir, Mr. Qian then asked for the resignation of the Party leadership, which was eventually accomplished with a vote, and then he stated that he intended to make China into a democratically elected, free market enterprise system, with freedom of religion, of the press, and of voting rights for all, if the Americans did not first destroy our nation."

"In short, he was elected the new leader, but unfortunately he was then shot to death right next to me, and so I was then elected the new leader in his place. What was done by our Communist Party leaders and our military leaders is almost beyond our comprehension and something that we all disavow and abhor. We admit that those leaders were behind these attacks and we're shamed beyond words."

At this point, Zhou's voice broke again, and his sobbing could be heard by all. Though his American listeners couldn't see them, Zhou continued as tears streamed down his face, his voice occasionally breaking. "Sir, we know our defensive weapons are useless against yours, and we no longer have any desire to fight your nation or your people in any form. I beg you, Sir, please, please, do not destroy our nation and our people. Sir, you have every right to demand retribution, although none that we can now give can ever replace your cities, your casualties, and your dead."

"Mr. President, you may take my life and the lives of the entire membership of the People's National Congress, plus all our top military leadership, as well. If that is not enough, you may destroy the same numbers that we took from you and an equal number of cities. I understand that the American public rightly wants revenge. You may move your military onto our soil wherever you wish, and I promise you no one shall oppose you. You might even wish to set up a McArthur-type military dictatorship over our nation, and that is equally acceptable."

"As you Americans like to say, the bottom line is that you can dictate any form of agreement you wish, and we shall comply. But I beg you to spare at least the portions of our population who were unaware of and innocent of these horrible deeds, as many of us were. I await your decision and reply, as we'll no longer oppose you in any manner. But time is of the essence, as I must try to form a government overnight, and arrest those who are certain to oppose us.

Once again, Mr. President, I plead, I beg, I ask forgiveness for the behavior of our former leaders, and we'll pay any price to rectify the wrongs that we have done to you and your people"

There was a long pause as President Warrington gathered his thoughts for a momentous and historic reply. He looked at the faces of those gathered in the room, and their expressions registered astonishment, sorrow, relief, incomprehension, partial anger, fear of deception, and pride, all rolled into such a mixture of thoughts, planning, and suggestions as to be difficult for Warrington to read. But the moistened eyes on some and the tears running down the faces of others, including his own, showed that they thought they had just heard a great man speak his heart out, and the pain and sorrow that they heard in his voice could not be duplicated by the best of actors.

Finally, the President wiped his eyes and replied. "Mr. Zhou, what shall we call you, as the title of leader seems inadequate?" Zhou, thankful for the President's thoughtful and diplomatic reply, said, "Sir, if I can form this new government, it will be along the lines of your own. With your permission, I shall use the title of the President of the United Provinces of China."

Warrington replied, "Then we agree that "Mr. President" shall be your title. You understand that we have to check all this out, and that I am going to have to try convince many in my country of a limit to the level of retaliation or retribution that will be acceptable to our angry American citizens."

"Yes, Mr. President", said Zhou, "I understand that you must ensure that my new government can in fact be established, and that many in your nation wish to destroy us all for what we have done, and further that we must pay whatever price your countrymen deem appropriate. I shall remain at this phone night and day awaiting your decisions and conditions to save our nation. I ask only one favor from you, Mr. President: please pray to your God for me, that I might be able to form this new government and convince all of the entrenched leaders to agree to your terms. I studied your Christian religions when I was in the U.S. studying business courses, and I believe that with our combined prayers, we might be able to somehow avoid the destruction of our nation." Zhou then said, "Goodbye, Mr. President, I hope our dilemmas can somehow be reconciled in the near future."

The old Chinese Admiral placed his hand on Zhou's shoulder and said, "You have done what was needed, however much it hurt, and you shall become a great leader of the Chinese people if we live through the American reprisals." Zhou noted through his own misty eyes that the Admiral's were also filled with tears of shame, sorrow, and relief.

The Americans Decide

After giving himself and everyone else time to compose themselves, Warrington asked for their comments. Erika Shultz, his Press Secretary, tears still streaming down her cheeks, was the first to comment. "Oh my God, we can't destroy all of China and all of its people. I know they hurt us badly, but the innocent and the children ..."

The White House Chief of Staff, Ralph Cutting, then spoke up. "Erika, this is far too important a matter for such emotional talk. Please just be quiet, because these issues are of global importance and the President needs our best assessment of Zhou's sincerity." Cutting then turned to the President and said, "Sir, I think he was honest, but my question is, can he pull this off before becoming a casualty himself?"

CIA Liaison Officer, Ed Pickings, next commented. "Mr. President, I can't provide any analysis or advice at this time. I mean: we have to ensure this isn't a ruse, or whether they might not have a secret weapon that's unknown to us at this point. I prefer not to comment on behalf of my Agency until we have time to get answers."

The President nodded and then turned to the last member of the group, FBI Liaison Officer, James Matthews. Matthews looked at Pickings and said, "Sir, I agree with Ed, in that however sincere Mr., or I should now say, President Zhou may seem on the phone, we still don't know enough about him or this supposed disillusionment within the Chinese Communist Party, to make heads or tails of it at this point. I'm aware that we're within hours of you giving the orders to our armed forces to lay waste to China, but we can spare some time to analyze all of this to gain a clearer picture, unless we're to believe they have new weapons that are comparable to our own. I personally don't think so, do you Ed?"

Pickings shook his head and said, "No, I don't think so, but I sure would hate to be wrong."

Matthews continued, "Well, I think we all agree, Mr. President, that we need more time, and I suggest we all reconvene in, say, five hours, which should allow time for the Joint Chiefs to be briefed on the new situation and whether or not you decide to delay the planned strikes."

With that the President stood, saying, "I agree, let's get it done."

It actually took six hours for them to reassemble in order to include the Joint Chiefs and the leaders of both the House and Senate in this discussion. Warrington stood before the group and spoke in a louder than normal voice. "Ladies and gentlemen, as you know, I insisted we return to the Capital as soon as possible after yesterday's WMD bombings in order not to appear cowardly and to encourage our population to keep the faith with their government leaders. As you also know, most of our Congressional members are spread across the nation, as are our military leaders to avoid a catastrophic decapitation of our national leadership."

"I had copies of the recorded phone call from President Zhou sent to General Paxton and his General Staff, along with abridged copies of our subsequent conversations. As you all know, I have placed the military on standby alert, but I am waiting for your views and comments before I reply to President Zhou. We haven't a lot of time for decision making before I have to call Zhou back and tell him my decision either to commence the war or to provide him with a list of demands and conditions that he and his new government must meet to avoid being destroyed. Before I begin, is there anything I should know?"

CIA Liaison Agent Pickings spoke up. "Mr. President, although the Middle East has been quiet up to now, we have very reliable information, learned from a recording, that a meeting was held in Damascus, Syria, attended by the top terrorist organizational leaders of Hamas, Hezbollah, and Al Qaeda. Basically, they were saying that, regardless of what happened in Iran, they will continue the war. They all agreed to disperse WMDs world-wide and then to set them off in any way they can, and wherever the local cell leaders choose to use them."

"Syria has a significant number of these weapons to begin with, and they plan to dig up those that were shipped to them at night by the old Saddam regime to avoid detection by our satellite coverage, and then take them over the borders however they can. They believe that once the weapons are outside of Syria, then they can commence using them whenever and wherever an opportunity exists. What they don't know is that our new satellites can see them at night just as easily as in the daytime, and we can nail them at any hidden site or military installation that attempts to move them. However, we only have five days before this plan is set to go into effect. Therefore, Mr. President, you must order Syria's destruction to prevent this."

Warrington paled for a moment, and then, seemingly angered and talking to himself, said, "Dammit, do they all want to be destroyed?" He shook his head as though to get his thinking straight, then turned to General Paxton and said, "Your thoughts, General?"

Without hesitating, Paxton said, "Sir, we can take out China the moment you give us the authority to do so. Hitting Syria will mean taking some of our planned assets from the Chinese war theater, but we can handle both, although I suggest you also ask my fellow officers for their views. Gentlemen?"

Harold Robinson, the Air Force Chief of Staff, responded first, saying, "Mr. President, we're ready to go and can obliterate both China and Syria with but a few adjustments to our ICBMs and Satellite Ray Guns. If we're going to hit both countries, though, we'll also have to rely on our manned bombers to ensure complete and total coverage of the targets, and we'll have to overlap with navy targeting. In short, the U.S. Air Force is ready and awaiting your authorization, and we can accomplish both missions." With that, Robinson looked at Admiral Bennett and nodded as though to say, your turn.

The Admiral looked at the President and said, "Sir, I'll need to redeploy several of our submarines, along with two of our carrier groups in order take up new attack positions. I'll need at least two and possibly three days, to make that happen. And though we carry nuclear weapons on the carrier aircraft, they're not as large as those the Air Force and Army intend to use all over China, and so we'll have to coordinate very closely with them in order to cover all of Syria, even with all the new weapons in our inventories."

"We also have to assume that accidents or breakdowns may occur, so to ensure total and complete coverage, I request a three-day delay to work out a new attack scenario and to insure the required coordination is complete and triple checked. I might add that some fallout from these weapons will drop over parts of Israel, so they must be warned. Thankfully, their citizens— unlike ours—are prepared for such an eventuality. That's all I have for you, Mr. President."

Next, the Commandant of the Marine Corps, Thomas Guy, was on deck. Guy looked at the Generals and Admiral Bennett and nodded his head as though to say, I understand what you're planning and might have to do. He began. "Mr. President, all I've heard thus far makes perfectly good sense militarily. But with your permission and indulgence, I would like to propose an alternative scenario for your consideration."

"For the record, I want to state that I completely agree with my colleagues and support all they have said. However, after hearing the phone call from Mr. Zhou, I thought of a different scenario, which revealed itself to me more clearly as we were being briefed on the new Syrian situation. My thought is that before we have China sign an unconditional surrender document, or else bomb them to kingdom come, why not make them pay for their attack on us this way."

"First, let's demand that they send their people worldwide to knock off all the known terrorists'—individuals, groups and cells—to acknowledge their complicity in this situation. Next, let's force them to engage and destroy Syria, under the pretense of the Syrians getting them into this situation in the first place.

Our people could monitor the results and be at the Chinese Military Headquarters in Beijing to watch them do it, and then monitor from our side and provide additional targets for them as we would for ourselves. The reasoning behind this is that we, the United States of America, could not be blamed for all that has befallen the Middle East nations, as now their former allies are complicit in attacks in that part of the world."

"Second, by observing the Chinese ICBMs and other weapons they might use, we can pinpoint other targets in China that we might have missed or that were hidden too deeply underground. Rather than destroy all of China, we can exact whatever revenge we desire and still possibly end up with a future ally. If what they say they plan to do is anywhere near right, we can have them handle some of the dirty work, and still not have to kill them all. That's my suggestion, but it's your call, Mr. President."

Chapter 14 – China Decides

19 October 2005 - China

The new Chinese President had trouble resting as he awaited the phone call and decision from President Warrington. Staring at his bloody clothing, Zhou kept recalling the assassination of his friend, Qian. But he refused to change his clothes or to shower, for fear of missing Warrington's call. He also listened to his friend, the old Admiral, who was advising him on what to do next to solidify his position and control their opposition. The old Admiral had placed a cot in the former Chairman's room, knowing that Zhou would not leave until he heard from the Americans; he also insured a new supply of food and drinks of the non-alcoholic kind, which were made available to the new Chinese President as the hours passed by.

During the long wait, both men knew that warring factions within the Chinese military and the government were lining up their allies, for the battle for the future leadership of China was certain to erupt very soon. The Admiral, now the new head of the Chinese military had sent orders for all forces to stand down, and for the troops to remain in their barracks unless called out under his personal orders only.

The military, still uncertain about exactly what had happened at the meeting of the Communist Party Congress, knew from rumors that a very big change had occurred and many leaders had been replaced. They also had heard that many of the top leaders remained under house arrest, and most surprisingly that the popular old Admiral who was admired and respected by most Chinese, had been named the new senior military leader. All this at a time when he had been expected to retire at his present rank, or possibly even to die in office of old age.

Senior officers, demanding to know the full story, were informed by the old Admiral that they would follow his orders and directives or be placed under house arrest, or even imprisoned. Not certain what to do since their seniors were unavailable and supposedly under house arrest, they grudgingly complied, which bought some more time for President Zhou.

While the military remained temporarily under control, the population became more brazen, with small riots breaking out in many parts of the nation. Because the Chinese police forces were also under orders to stand down they were unable to nip the riots in the bud, which grew in intensity while the police and the military remained close to their stations or barracks. Eventually some forces were allowed to deploy to control the riots, when the old Admiral relented on special requests, and then only in specific locations.

President Zhou and the old Admiral tried to anticipate every conceivable demand the Americans might make of them and they both wondered if there would be any room for negotiation, or if the Americans would simply do as they had done with the Japanese and the Germans and demand unconditional surrender. They had contemplated every possible scenario and demand they could imagine however outlandish and degrading, and even then they knew they could not think of all the possibilities and eventualities. So they decided they must find others to help, for Zhou's answers and agreements with the Americans, as they were going to have long-lasting and most profound effects on China and its people for the foreseeable future. They knew that they could not make these momentous and frightening decisions alone, and tried to think of those whom they could trust to assist in these most desperate and demeaning circumstances left to them by their former leaders.

They began naming individuals, but they both knew by having been raised in a Communist regime for most of the Admiral's adult life and all of Zhou's life, that they might find a few trustworthy underlings and some college professors. But none who could be counted on to accept or even understand the concept of forming a new nation under democratic rules of law, or of allowing opposition political parties and everything that goes with those concepts.

Nor would some ever accept the defeat of their nation without even a token fight by the largest standing army in the world. Of course, most were completely unaware of the terrible weapons the Americans possessed, and even if Zhou and the Admiral could explain what China was facing in rather simple terms, some would still elect to fight.

After lengthy discussion of these issues, they concluded that they had only two choices. They could make the decisions themselves on behalf of China, just as the Japanese Emperor had done during the Japanese surrender to the Americans in 1945. Or they must reconvene an emergency session of the People's Congress and plead with them—the former Representatives of the Chinese people—to allow Zhou to make these decisions for the sake of the nation, or else through whatever was decided in the Congressional meeting by the representatives and delegates as there was no longer a Central Committee to guide them.

An even worse scenario occurred to them: what if the Americans' phone call came during this meeting; what could they say to them? That they were debating the issues and would get back to them later? No, that was not the solution, and they were running out of options on what to do and how to do it. Yes, they had removed the Communist Party leadership and had elected Zhou after the death of Qian. But Zhou had not yet been given complete authority to negotiate China's fate with the Americans or even to appoint subordinates, as the meeting had ended right after electing Zhou to his new position–and even that was under the title of Leader, not Chairman or President, the title suggested by the American President, Warrington.

Zhou sometimes felt as though he were undergoing his final exams again in America for his Master's degrees, where he had had to think logically in Chinese while answering the questions in English, either orally or in writing. Then, his mind had switched from language to language, back and forth and back and forth, just as his mind now raced through the kaleidoscope of very recent events, conversations, suggestions, ideas, replies, horror, astonishment, anger, tears, shock, elation however temporary, confusion as to options, and fear as to the possibilities. He felt as though he had gone through practically every emotion he had ever had in the past, and still it never seemed to end.

Similarly, the old Admiral had gone through his share of emotions and confusion. But being older and wiser, he knew they must both present a unified front if this new government was to survive through the next hours, never mind days, weeks, or months. To think further than that was beyond the Admiral's abilities, and he also knew that if they were not able to hold on and convince the majority of delegates to support them, they would all soon be dead: either from the Americans or from whomever took over the leadership role, because they would both be labeled traitors to the Communist Party and the Chinese people.

The old Admiral never spoke of it, but he had always secretly admired the Americans, even if they sometimes did foolish things and got involved in situations where they might have been better off had they left things alone. He also had some family members who were saved from the Japanese in WWII and somehow got passage to America because they had helped the Americans in that war, which had made them eligible to emigrate.

He was in touch with only one relative to avoid being compromised by either side, and knew that all his relatives were college graduates, owned businesses or were senior business officials, and all seemed quite happy in the U.S. Now, he was awaiting the possibility of being destroyed by the one nation and people that he admired beyond his own. In any case, remembering the past would not resolve the present issues at hand, and so the Admiral suggested to Zhou that he, the Admiral, call an emergency session of the People's Congress to explain the true situation to all Representatives and delegates, as well as explaining why Zhou could not attend.

This seemed like as good a plan as any to Zhou, as he had run out of ideas and believed that there was no choice but to ask that he be allowed to negotiate for the nation, or there might not be a nation left to negotiate about.

The Admiral sent out the word for the People's Congress to meet again in 45 minutes, as the members had not gone far from the hall. They were still attempting to understand what they had agreed to and voted on in the first session and had no idea what to do next, or if they even had a job or position any longer.

The meeting reconvened, and the Admiral took the former Chairman's seat to address the assembly. He began by explaining that they were not to be concerned with their jobs, as the new government would view their services to the old regime favorably, and there would be a place for all in the new government. Initially, there was clapping and smiling as they understood that they would still retain authority and positions in the new government, which meant a continuing paycheck, whatever that might turn out to be.

But then several members realized that the Admiral was speaking and sitting in the chair that Leader Zhou should have been occupying. Before the Admiral could continue, a representative rose and asked in an accusing voice, "Where is our elected leader?" The Admiral replied that Zhou was in the former Chairman's office, awaiting a phone call from the American President. That answer did not satisfy the representatives. So to show them that Zhou was not also under arrest, the Admiral allowed a delegation, under guard, to visit Zhou, and held the meeting up to await the delegation's return and report.

When they met with Zhou, they received his partial explanation about why he had to remain there, and so they returned and reported to the assembly that Zhou was not under arrest, but was under great pressure from the Americans, which was why the Admiral now led the meeting of the People's Congress.

The Admiral then continued explaining what was actually going on. The stunned audience heard what their nation's dilemma was and why there was little time or even good cause for debate. If they did not give Zhou the authority to speak for China, the Americans would surely attack and very soon, and the Chinese military was incapable of stopping them. The Admiral also informed them that the Americans' demands were unknown at this time, and that was why the Leader now awaited the American President's phone call. They had to decide right here and now whether to trust Zhou to negotiate for them, or face Iran's fate.

The old Admiral then asked them to vote to allow Zhou to represent all of China, because if they did not they would all face the coming destruction of their nation and possibly all or most of their people. Fortunately, the vote gave Zhou the permission he had sought. The old Admiral sent a runner to inform the new Leader of their decision, and Zhou was relieved that that crisis was over. He rested his head on his hands as the Admiral entered the room and sat down next to him to explain that the representatives and delegates were on a break, as no further business could be conducted until they knew what had occurred between the two Presidents.

They were discussing who should be assigned to the various government positions and agreed that a new Constitution would have to be written, when the phone rang. They knew the President of the United States would be on the line.

Zhou then did something he had seen done countless times in the past while in the U.S. and other foreign countries, but had never done himself. He didn't quite understand why he was doing it, but he made the sign of the cross across his head and chest, just as he had seen Christians do so many times before. And then he reached for the phone.

Chapter 15 – No Options for China, Syria Pays

18 October 2005 - Washington, D. C.

President Warrington had heard General Guy's recommendation with a new appreciation of the General and his Marines. Warrington had always viewed the Marines with some disdain as they tended from his past experiences to be overly aggressive, and so he had never had thought of them as being either politically or diplomatically astute. But twice in a very short period, the Marine Commandant had provided an answer or at least a reasonable solution, to a most difficult world wide crisis. Warrington thought now that the Joint Chief's Chairman should have been General Guy, but he knew that the Marine Corps—the smallest of the services—would always be bested by supporters of the other military branches in any run for the JCS Chairmanship. However, this man who had seen much of war, sounded more like someone who belonged in the State Department or in a university or even a think tank. But his craggy face and military bearing, along with his perfectly-fitted uniform, made him a standout from the other JCS members, although none of them appeared to notice.

The Commandant was right. If the U.S. could entice a third party—besides Israel—to destroy Syria, then no one could blame the U.S. for all the death and destruction wrought on the world in recent weeks. Furthermore, China had little choice in the matter at this stage of the unfolding events.

The discussions continued to center around General Guy's proposals, and in the end, the Air Force and Army leaders thought it a bad plan. They were already prepared to strike China to repay them for the 2,126,000 dead and those dying each day from the WMD weapons used against the U.S., weapons that were unquestionably under the control and leadership of the Chinese government. No, these two services wanted revenge, not the mollycoddling methods the Marine Corps Commandant suggested to get the Chinese off the hook. But the Navy and the CIA and FBI Liaisons all sided with General Guy.

The President then asked about the whereabouts of the FBI and the CIA Directors at this moment of crisis. CIA Liaison Pickings and FBI Liaison Officer Matthews informed him that their bosses were in secure areas to prevent the decapitation of the entire leadership of the U.S. government. Warrington said, "I don't think that's right, since we're all here in Washington." Matthews then spoke up. "Mr. President, you knew when you placed those men in those unique and important positions that you had selected two weak-kneed sisters in order to pay back political favors and to placate Senator Pelerine and Representative Albertson, and you now see the results of that decision."

Barney Albertson stood up and shouted, "I object to Agent Matthews' comments, and I want him fired right here and now!" Before the President could interject, Ed Pickings spoke first and said, "Agent Matthews is not only right, I support him all they way, and we are both prepared to resign or be fired if the President wants that. But you, sir, are nothing more than a fat, obnoxious, egotistical empty suit, a man who hasn't the slightest idea of what is really happening in this room. I suggest you sit down and listen to what people in the know are saying, and that includes you, too, Senator Pelerine. Barney, if you open your mouth once more, I will personally place my foot in your backside where the sun don't shine."

The room was so quiet after this startling outburst that it took a minute for all to recover from Pickings' words. The President stood, and half smiling at the two embarrassed Congressional leaders, said, "Barney and Susan, I will not fire either of these men or ask for their resignations, as they've just said what I've often longed to say but never had the nerve or guts to do. You two are here only for window dressing because neither of you is capable of comprehending the situation we now find ourselves involved with, nor of the terrible decisions I am now faced with making. You may both remain, but I don't want to hear another word from either of you, is that clear?"

They both nodded in the affirmative but with bowed heads, as the President seemed to see right through their phony political thoughts and their personal desires, and to take for credit for things they had claimed to do for the nation in the past.

They had always supported left wing causes, and through their political and business connections had acquired much wealth over their lifetimes. But their true values and beliefs were quite different from those they promoted to the public and everyone but they themselves seemed to understand that as a truism.

People like Barney and Susan were products of political favors and political correctness, just like the former Secretaries of Defense and State under the Clinton administration. They were bumblers with no special talents who had made the grade though political shenanigans and paybacks; and while they appeared acceptable in times of relative peace they were disasters in times of peril or crisis. Barney and Susan now realized their limitations and lack of true leadership and knowledge in the areas of concern that they had mostly avoided or ignored. The chickens had come to roost, and they would no longer be viewed as they had hoped to be.

Finally, the President said, "Ladies and gentlemen, I completely agree with General Guy's suggestions, although I intend to tweak them just a bit. But the basic concept will be carried out, and I order you all to comply with my directives, which will be in your hands shortly. Are there any questions or comments?"

The room was quiet, and as the President's nod to them indicated that the meeting was over, he told them that he now had to make his demands known to the Chinese President. He then asked the JCS members and the FBI and CIA Liaisons to remain to witness this conversation.

It took 30 more minutes to discuss some of the specific demands and exactly how the Chinese were to carry out both the attacks on the terrorists world-wide and the massive attack on Syria, and then afterwards to dismantle their own military and weapons to a level of defense approved by the U.S. President. While specifics would require more time to prepare, the basic requirements would be disclosed to Zhou and the old Admiral, and a new hotline with the U.S. and Chinese militaries would be established to insure that no mistakes were made regarding the intended targets, or that the missiles were somehow sent in the wrong directions. The U.S. planned to track each missile shot or bomb dropped.

A similar hotline would be established between the CIA and FBI and their Chinese counterparts in order to track the destruction of the terrorist groups, individuals or their cells. Additionally, the Chinese must account for all WMDs provided to the terrorists in the past, and no excuses would be allowed for not knowing exactly who had them. Furthermore, the leaders and their cronies from Brazil, Cuba, Ecuador, Venezuela, and Bolivia would be "dispatched" by Chinese assassin squads. Any other Latino countries found to be supporting the terrorists could expect the same treatment of their leaders.

The die was cast and the phone call completed. President Zhou recorded and wrote down all of the conditions required of him, which included allowing new U.S. military bases to be located throughout China.

Zhou appealed for a more reasonable solution, as he had no desire to do the dirty work of the U.S., that is, for the Chinese government to kill millions of Syrians. But his balks at each demand were met with the threat to accept all or nothing. There would be no negotiations or compromises, the U.S. President was adamant in that regard, and Zhou, looking at the old Admiral with horror, watched as the Admiral nodded his head yes to each demand.

So there were no options available to the Chinese: it was either allow China to be destroyed, or have the Chinese military destroy Syria. While he thought it was an astounding, agonizing, and evil proposal by the U.S. government, the large loss of American lives was not even allowed to be a topic of political debate. The Americans wanted revenge, and China, as the perpetrator and leader of the attacks on the Americans, was left with little room to maneuver.

Zhou knew he must agree or all of China would be destroyed, and they had no way now to fight back or protect themselves. So he agreed to the demands, and as new leaders were quickly appointed to their positions of responsibility in the new Chinese government, they were briefed on the actions that the Chinese nation had agreed to perform.

Only five people, including three military commanders who had been selected and later briefed on the upcoming events, chose to resign their positions and return to their homes. They were quickly replaced by others more willing, and so the Chinese military re-targeted its weapons, and the Chinese Special Forces and espionage operatives received their marching orders to assassinate the various Latino and Muslim political or religious leaders.

22 October 2005

By October 22nd, 2005 (U.S. time), a period of only four days, everything was ready, and the plans were in place. The lines of communications between the Chinese and the Americans were established and tested on the first day of the notifications. Now, all that was required was for the U.S. President to give the order to begin the planned events. It seemed to both the Chinese and Americans alike a dreamlike rush to worldwide warfare and destruction, with the Chinese in the vanguard of the terrible events that were about to unfold.

President Warrington had had a difficult time with the Israelis, as they knew they would incur heavy casualties with all the nukes and biological and chemical agents being dropped on Syria. But the President would not relent and finally said, "Prepare your people as the war is now underway, and we have no choice in this matter anymore than you do and will send help as soon as we can, but events can no longer be contained. I will pray for you and your people."

With a heavy heart and a prayer for God's forgiveness, the man who no longer wished to be the President of the U.S. called Zhou, a man wishing he was no longer the President of China, and spoke the fateful words: "The plan is now approved and operational, and God forgive and help us all." Upon hearing those spoken words, Zhou gave his own order to his countrymen, and the forces of destruction moved forward without the least hesitation or remorse for what had to be done.

It only took 36 hours to destroy all of Syria. The casualties far exceeded the projections of the Chinese and American war planners. All targets were destroyed several times over, and there was no resistance to speak of, as the Syrian military and the civil population was completely unprepared for the onslaught.

The leaders and many of their underlings from Cuba, Venezuela, Bolivia, and Ecuador were also assassinated, but the leader and confidants of the Brazilian government went into hiding in the massive jungles of the Amazon region, leaving its government rudderless and panicked.

The fallout from the nukes used in Syria swept across vast regions of the world via the trade winds. It was even found dispersed across India and Pakistan, and all the way to the American continent, but by then, its lethality had diminished and most were saved with the new medications.

Seemingly overnight, the world was transformed from one of conflict and hatred to a new world in which the multitudes understood the very high price that must be paid for its laxity in allowing those promoting hatred and discontent to reach the positions of leadership. The entire world would soon be eager to find ways to resolve future issues and disputes, but for now, they remained fearful that they might be next.

It was not long before reports emerged from China of the deaths of thousands of Communist leaders, as well as a good number of Chinese military officers and espionage operatives. Next, the Palestinians suddenly were eager to discuss mutual boundaries with the Israelis and the North Koreans likewise with their Southern neighbors. Vietnam and Cuba renounced their Communist governments and began the process of becoming democracies. Similarly, the Pakistanis and Indians sought an end to the Kashmir crisis, and both sides soon gave up some portions to achieve a mutually-agreeable border. The Muslims of the former Soviet Union provinces seemed much more conciliatory toward the Russians, and a new attitude toward accepting territorial agreements was in the making.

April 2006

Within six months, the world community of nations, though still recovering from the after effects of the recent wars, was seeing many formerly oppressive and authoritarian societies beginning to accept freedoms and religious tolerance never thought possible in the past. Pessimism and hatred were now being held in check for a much larger number of people than before. But the most positive aspect was that the words and actions of liberals and activists of all nations, still bent on causing trouble and havoc, were now being ignored by the vast majority of their people, and the demeaning and vitriolic attacks on national leaders were now being muted and condemned by the various media outlets.

A majority of citizens now objected to communistic and socialistic propaganda as never before. Even Hollywood began to make movies commending the American leadership for its generosity in not destroying China, as now the world knew that China and the Islamist terrorists were behind the losses of millions of American citizens.

The world's communities now saw what modern warfare could bring upon people and their nations, and they no longer had any stomach for it. Islam would soon lose its hold on its billion plus followers, as Muslims were more and more exposed to other ideals, beliefs, and philosophies that was previously suppressed and not permitted to be discussed.

And just as the Christians and Jews had questioned their own past teachings and beliefs, Muslims were now starting to find the errors and fallacies within their own religious scriptures, along with resolutions to areas previously marked by misunderstanding, conflict of meaning, or word interpretations.

True, the world was far from perfect in this emerging more open era of enlightenment, and much still remained to be done to allow many nations to progress into joining the world's more enlightened communities. They also had to find alternatives, solutions and compromises for those areas of conflict that still existed. The UN was not completely dead, rather—like the mythical Phoenix bird—it had reemerged from the ashes of recent conflicts.

However, this new group of nations would be transparent to the world, and secret deals and corruption would be punished most severely. Further, any member state found guilty of a return to the old behavior would be suspended, that is, until a vote could be taken by all member nations to approve its reinstatement. One single "No" vote could preclude reentry into the new organization. The new organization was called the Free and Democratic Nations of the World, and any who did not fit the meaning of the new name need not apply.

France and Germany had attempted to form their own group of United Nations, but that effort soon failed, as even the smaller countries of Europe preferred the American version to either the old UN or the European model. America was now viewed in a more positive light by much of the world just as it had been after WWII; mainly for its generosity and new Marshall type plans to help everyone including former enemies.

For several years, the American light of freedom and free enterprise was hailed as a new breakthrough in world relations and human understandings. The world could look forward to a brighter tomorrow and an optimistic future for all mankind. But troubles were gathering on the horizon, and soon the world would begin a new round of warfare and destruction, as the evil leaders of certain nations refused to join in the world's praise of the U.S.

The news came from an obscure news media outlet that had traced the sources of incomes of the wealthiest families in the world. In doing so, they had uncovered some startling news that eventually sent shivers down the spines of American political leaders and those of senior military officers as well.

Chapter 16 – The New World in Crisis

2008

For several years, the people of the world seemed outwardly content due to the dramatic agreements and treaties forged by many nations and groups that had previously seemed to have irreconcilable, cultural, religious, tribal, territorial, racial, or ethnic differences.

Additionally, the leaders of all major religions had met in Istanbul and agreed to allow all that was wrong with their own religious histories to be aired with criticism and without rancor or opposition. The idea was that by doing so, they would learn from one another and be better able to understand and accept that no one religion provided the only pathway to heaven, and further that all had sinned dreadfully at one time or another. This needed to be expressed so that a truer and more tolerant religious base could be established within each form or type of religion.

Naturally, there were smaller schisms of zealots and the intolerant, but they too would someday be ignored by the majority of the citizenry, and their followers would soon move on to the larger and more acceptable religious institutions. This gave hope to all who had lived through a very intolerant and very divisive world period.

The airing of the history of the old Jewish kingdoms and their often cruel punishments were laid bare for all to see and it was then discussed. The Christians presented the Church's crimes: from the Crusades to the Inquisition; from the European wars against the Catholic Church all the way through the movement away from Europe and to the burning of witches in the city of Salem, Massachusetts, in America. The Muslims also spoke out about the sins of Mohammed and the Muslims' attempt to capture and forcefully convert the Christians of Europe and the Hindus of India to Islam.

The losses in people and properties from religious wars had been of enormous and unknowable proportions, but everyone concurred that this must never be allowed to happen again regardless of which religion might be in the majority. Also, English was being taught as a secondary language around the world and all agreed this was best for their citizens. For when America finally recovered from its human, property and financial losses, it would continue to lead the world in business, science, medicine, and industries yet to be created. The ability to understand English as the world's primary language was considered by most national leaders as a necessity that would enable them to better compete on the global markets.

And all had been going well, until an obscure Australian newspaper reporter discovered a plot by the world's most wealthy citizens, a plot of clearly evil intent and of worldwide dimensions. What the reporter had gained through interviews with the world's richest citizens was quite interesting to him, but seemed barely newsworthy to others.

However, he noted that some who had been moderately rich before were now becoming very wealthy and indeed seemingly overnight, and so he began his own investigation with some help from colleagues and then began to unravel the new plot.

It had begun, not unsurprisingly to most with the French elite and intellectuals, and carried on through to the wealthiest of the world. Groups of intellectuals had always formed semi-secret societies, at least in recent history. These were not the Aristotle's and Plato's of the ancient world, but rather those who considered themselves far beyond the norm intellectually. They viewed the world as a place whereby the masses had to be led by superior minds, lest they attempt to reach the levels of the more educated and gifted. Most of these intellectuals were insufferable egotists and elitists who honestly believed that because of their privileged educations, breeding and wealth, that only they should determine how mankind should live and be rewarded.

To accept the crude and unrefined Americans as the world's leader was almost beyond their comprehension. While eager to dispense sage advice to those advancing to replace them as age and infirmities took their toll, they believed almost to the last individual that only France could lead the world in the right direction and establish the proper standards for the rest of those lacking in intellectual knowledge. They alone had the means and minds to make changes in the world that were truly relevant, at least in their old world eyes.

For all their supposed intellect, they remained enamored with the writings of Marx and Engle, and even with Lenin. They were rather clever individuals who could tell rarely-published and naughty stories of the risqué behaviors of French writers and artists such as Voltaire, Rousseau, Rene' Descartes, Edgar Degas, Claude Monet, Frederic Brazille, and many others. This endeared them to the many who felt inferior to these rich and pompous so-called intellectuals.

An American actress not known for her intellect had once met long ago with these same people on a trip to France, and she had quickly accepted their entire anti-American line. She had then gone to Vietnam to oppose a war that the French had originally instigated, and then she became infamous throughout America for her smiling photo while seated on the enemy's anti-aircraft gun. Others from many other countries had been similarly misled by these groups of French elites, and these Frenchmen and women had marveled at how easy it was to convince these people of little consequence to be in awe of them. This was based primarily on their wealth and their clever insights into outmoded and failed intellectual exercises, rather than on true friendships.

This so-called elite group honestly believed it had all the answers to mankind's problems, and therefore, logically should lead the world with their views and their wealth. Many of these tycoons of the French Republic secretly longed for a Royal regime such as the one that England still enjoyed, but were thwarted in this endeavor because the foolish people of France would not accept another monarchy, at least not yet.

So they had set out secretly to influence the future. They did this by insisting that even their own President and other senior officials, whom they had cleverly pushed into positions of power through their wealth and influence, treat Americans with respect, dignity, and courtesy. They had bought jobs and senior positions in the American companies that had produced the new laser and radio wave weapons that helped win the last war. These "employees" soon stole the American's technology secrets and embarked on massive research and production programs of these same weapons. Soon, they were selling them to all who wished them. The naive and trusting Americans, whom the French had so recently groveled over as though in awe of them, were fooled by the new French attitude and had quickly accepted this newfound relationship.

Meanwhile, the French government had long ago given up limiting the number of Muslim immigrants allowed into their nation, and the demographics had changed so much in such a short period of time, that Muslims now controlled many of the French Provinces and held many of the key positions in government. From there, they were able to manipulate polices and directives for their own purposes. No, the War with Islam was not over, and the French were behind the next wave of terrorists that would soon emerge with the new weapons.

The U.S. had foolishly allowed the French once again to join the new collection of free and democratic nations, even though the French had proven over, and over, and over again their deceitful and anti-American, not to mention anti-Israeli and anti-British nature. There seemed no sensible way to placate the French leadership: once they had the new weapon systems, they returned to their old ways of arrogance, deceit, and a complete lack of appreciation for what had been done for them by so many in the past, and especially by the Americans.

Reports began coming in that these new weapons, of French origin, were being found in Africa, the Middle East, and the old Soviet Union's now predominately Muslim provinces. The no-longer new American President, once so pleased with the progress of the world's nations in finding common ground through compromise and major reductions in conflicts throughout the world, now found that his new French ally was inciting a new arms race. He worried that the dispersion of these new weapons must be stopped and very soon, or else there would be dire consequences for the entire world.

The President pondered this situation, and then called for a meeting of his personal Staff and Cabinet, along with the Joint Chiefs of Staff. General Thomas Guy, the Commandant of the Marine Corps, was the first military leader to arrive.

Further Reading

In the 18 months since I began researching and writing the WMD Guide and writing this book, the news has been full of reports that provide further evidence supporting the primary concerns that motivated me to begin these projects.

In this section, I have provided pointers to some of the more recent news stories; books and commentaries that further demonstrate the seriousness of the continued lack of preparedness of the American public for any type of WMD incident, which these reports indicate are increasingly likely if the countries involved remain unchecked.

Those readers who are interested in learning more about the 'real politics' behind the situations and alliances in this book, or who want to verify the accuracy of the scenarios in the novel, may be interested in some further reading shown below.

News Stories, Books and Commentaries

- America the Vulnerable: How Our Government Is Failing to Protect Us from Terrorism, by Stephen Flynn, HarperCollins, August 1, 2004, ISBN: 0060571284, Hardcover: 256 pp.

- China tests ballistic missile submarine-Wash Times www.washingtontimes.com/national/20041202-115302-2338r.htm

- China, Cuba Seek Economic Links www.cnsnews.com/ViewForeignBureaus.asp?Page=/ForeignBureaus/archive/200411/FOR20041123b.html

- Chinese presence on island viewed with concern
  www.washingtontimes.com/world/20041208-095901-3064r.htm

- Cuban Policy In The Middle East: A Cuba-Iran Axis ?
  www.cartadecuba.org/cuba-iran_axis.htm

- *Iran threatens 'Top Secret' counter-attacks*, Dec. 4, 2004
  www.wnd.com/news/article.asp?ARTICLE_ID=41760

- *Iran, China Forming Major Alliance*
  www.newsmax.com/archives/articles/2004/11/17/83609.shtml

- *Iranian 'Sputnik' Trojan Horse*
  www.newsmax.com/archives/ic/2004/11/28/182924.shtml

- Muslim Scholars Increasingly Debate Unholy War [registration required for access]
  www.nytimes.com/2004/12/10/international/middleeast/10islam.html?oref=regi

- *One Reporter's Opinion - The Systematic Dismantling of America,* George Putnam
  Friday, Dec. 3, 2004
  www.newsmax.com/archives/articles/2004/12/3/91028.shtml

- *Pakistan's Most Dangerous Man*
  www.newsmax.com/archives/articles/2004/12/3/15702.shtml

- *Planned Cleanup for Dirty Bombs Called Lax*
  www.newsmax.com/archives/articles/2004/12/3/
  104427.shtml

- *Powell – Iran Is Trying to Fit Missiles for Nukes*
  www.newsmax.com/archives/articles/2004/11/1
  8/90133.shtml

- President Of Vet Organization Calls For Revival
  Of Mutually Assured Destruction As Only
  Defense Against Nuclear Attack www.i-
  served.com/v-v-a-
  r.org/121104_NuclearTerror.html

- Radical Islam and LNG in Trinidad and Tobago
  www.iags.org/n1115045.htm

- Sarin Gas - Wonder Why You Haven't Heard
  About This?
  www.boortz.com/nuze/200411/11172004.html

- *Terror Expert – Qaida WMD Attack On US
  Likely Soon*
  www.jpost.com/servlet/Satellite?pagename=JPo
  st/JPArticle/ShowFull&cid=1101615867007

- *The Latin American Bloc: The Ignored Danger
  to Freedom*
  www.worldthreats.com/latin_america/Latin%20
  American%20Danger.htm

- The Naked Communist, by Cleon Skousen,
  Buccaneer Books Inc; Reprint edition, June 1,
  1994, ISBN: 1568493673, Hardcover.

- *The Rise of Chinese Military Power*
  www.newsmax.com/archives/articles/2004/12/1/
  152935.shtml

- The 1958 Communist Goals, excerpted from The Naked Communist, pp. 259-262 and also published in the 1963 Congressional Record (reproduced in 1999 on WorldnetDaily.com in a commentary by Geoff Metcalf) www.wnd.com/news/article.asp?ARTICLE_ID=19566
A significant number of the 45 goals listed here have already been achieved without most of the American public noticing it over the past 40-50 years.

- *Understaffed RCMP can't fight terror–Report: Mounties may receive tip about attack but be unable to act* www.canada.com/national/nationalpost/news/newsletter/story.html?id=6f40bd8c-64a0-431c-827d-29a886aab980

- U.S. Plans to Help Young Victims of Terrorism Are Criticized – NY Times www.anbex.com/articles/new_page_54.htm

- U.S. Unprepared Despite Progress, Experts Say- Wash Post www.washingtonpost.com/nation

- War in 2020, by Ralph Peters, Pocket; Reprint edition January 1, 1992, ISBN: 0671751727, 624 pp.

Medals of Heroes

(To the Troops)

Our nation gives out medals
For our wounded and our dead
Made of metal, cloth, and plastic
For the blood that they have shed
So many Hero medals
Rarely given the common men
Who fought the many ugly wars
Just a note on history's pen
Seniors often quick to tell you
Of the medals on their chest
Are worn for deeds of other men
Unknown to all the rest
It seems so strange, so many fell
And the wounded that returned
No awards were ever offered
For the dead, the maimed, the burned
Did so many do so little
That their deeds remain unknown
Is their just reward a Purple Heart,
A grave, a white headstone
Didn't anybody see them
When they joined our nation's call
Didn't anybody hear them
When they gave their soul, their all

Were we all so very busy
To recall the scared who tried
To let us live another day
Many wounded, many died
Combat medals often junior
To the ones that seniors wear
Are seniors blind to those who fought
Or don't they really care?

By Major Frank C. Stolz, USMC (Retired)

© 2003

About the Author

Major Frank Stolz is a retired Marine Corps Officer who spent twenty years in the Corps, a good portion of that overseas. A Vietnam veteran, he commanded Marine Rifle Platoons and a Rifle Company in combat and later held duties as an Advisor to Republic of Vietnam (RVN) Forces. His tours of duty also included tours at HQMC, the Pentagon, as well as a tour in the Military Assistance Advisory Group (MAAG) China. Upon retiring in 1979, Major Stolz worked for another 13 years in Saudi Arabia with the oil company Aramco, and then spent five more years in other Middle and Far Eastern nations. He is a graduate of San Diego State University. Now retired, he resides in Texas. You can read other samples of his writing and commentaries on his website, www.wmdterror.com

With another retired Marine Corps veteran, CWO-4 James E. Mulloy, USMC (Ret.), Major Stolz has also written and published a tutorial on home remedies and strategies to protect families from WMD attacks, which is included as a non-fiction companion piece to the novel.

"America has no empire to extend or utopia to build. We wish for others only what we wish for ourselves – safety from violence, the rewards of liberty, and the hope for a better life."

President George W. Bush, Speech to West Point graduates, June 1, 2002

Home Remedies and Protection for Weapons of Mass Destruction (WMD) Incidents

Prepared by

Major Frank C. Stolz, USMC (Retired), Round Rock TX
CWO-4 James E. Mulloy, USMC (Ret.), Oceanside, CA

www.WMDTerror.com

This section is a <u>non-fiction</u> supplement to the novel, "WMD Attacks on America!" in order to educate readers about actions they should take or avoid in the event of a nearby WMD attack, accompanied by recommended home remedies and resources they can acquire now to begin preparing for such an occurrence.

Disclaimer

The authors do not have medical backgrounds or any vast amount of Atomic/Nuclear, Biological, and Chemical training beyond their military training and experiences. We state categorically that the information presented here is NOT recommended as a means of diagnosing or treating any illness, and that we believe all WMD-related illnesses should be referred to a medical physician or a medical center.

Since the original document was published in 2003 (privately and over the Internet), we have continued to observe the Federal government's actions (or lack thereof) in these areas and have finally decided to make this basic information available to a broader segment of the general public through the opportunity presented by the publication of this book. It seems reasonable to include the tutorial as a companion non-fiction piece that may be helpful to the readers of this book, although it is considered to be a literary no, no.

Our hope is that this guide will increase your ability to survive a WMD incident if one occurs near you. We hope it will never be needed, but if it is, this would be the greatest gift that we could ever give you. Please remember: you should always check with other medical sources to verify this data and to adjust it to your particular needs.

Foreword

This companion to the preceding novel is a safety and protection guide for all Americans, as well as for citizens of other nations. I encourage you to keep it handy in case any actual WMD incidents occur in your location.

This guide provides information about the various WMD agents believed to be in the possession of our enemies, along with some suggested remedies for treatment that include traditional medications as well as some suggested alternative and even holistic remedies and medications.

The guide also provides email addresses and some important telephone numbers for key government agencies so you can confirm the information presented here if you care to check it out.

Finally, it describes various courses of actions that you and your family might use in the event of a WMD incident in your vicinity, and to provide a greater degree of protection than you might otherwise have considered.

Major Frank C. Stolz, USMC (Ret.)

December 2004

www.WMDTerror.com

Preface

The safety precautions and home remedies described in this document were written for use by the family members of the authors.

We developed this document originally as a simple tutorial solely for use by our immediate family members who might become frightened, impaired, panic stricken or simply unsure of what to do. That is, in case they are notified that they are in a location where a WMD device has been activated and they are unable to leave that particular area. The document covers only basic safety information on protection and possible treatment of injuries from, atomic/ nuclear blasts, biological agents, and chemical agents.

We began it with our families in mind, and then expanded its audience focus as others asked for copies. Eventually, it became a project at the start of the war in Iraq (Iraqi Freedom) in early 2003, as something we might provide for the troops and their families. In the fall of 2003, it was published on the Internet at www.AmericasVoices.org as an e-book available for the general public, and with the caveat that we do NOT recommend information as a means of diagnosing or treating any illness. We believe and recommend that all WMD-related illnesses should be referred to a medical physician or a medical center.

Neither of us has a medical background or any vast amount of atomic/nuclear, biological, and chemical training beyond our military training and experiences. But after researching the subject over a four month period, we both came to the conclusion that the American government has not prepared its citizens for this type of warfare and does not have sufficient trained resources, medications, or antidotes for the average American to count on if WMD incidents were to occur in their locations.

This type of disaster can occur because government officials, wishing to limit the spread of a communicable agent might prevent citizens from leaving a given area, or alternatively, panic-stricken civilians may clog the streets and freeways thereby making traffic mobility impossible.

In fact, it seems to us that government officials at all levels have avoided training and preparing American citizens in basic self-protection, and therefore the public can only hope for assistance after an event occurs - when assistance may be least readily available. We are not aware of any recommended home remedies or optional medications proposed in any Defense Preparedness Plans (prepared by county, city, state, and federal authorities) or of any other source that could be distributed on an after-the-fact basis.

The material presented here is simply information about the different types of WMDs that might be used by terrorists, and some steps that average citizens can take to protect their families both before and after such attacks. We are not experts; anyone can find this information if they take the time to do the research, but most people do not have the time nor the means to sort and sift through the voluminous mounds of information on the government web sites.

We have assembled the information presented here from numerous government and other public sources, including reports from the Centers for Disease Control and Prevention (CDC), the Federal Emergency Management

Agency (FEMA), and numerous books, articles and websites. All of these are listed in the Appendix. We intended this to be simple: it includes a list of precautions and procedures to follow, avoids most medical and specialty terminology and acronyms, and lists the information in the manner we think our family members will be most able to respond to, prepare for, and use, should they encounter a WMD incident.

We want to stress that you should use the information given here ONLY if you are unable to locate and receive medical assistance or emergency help during any such situation, and is geared specifically towards a WMD incident. In all probability, this information will never be needed or used, and it is therefore provided only as a precaution to avoid any unnecessary panic.

Some History Regarding This Document

The increased terrorist threat after 9/11 should have been a wake-up call to all Americans, and particularly to our military and civilian emergency response organizations. We read during the research for this document that the Nuclear, Biological, and Chemical Protective Clothing and Gas Masks issued to the above organizations are now in question by experts, regarding their actual protective usefulness as well as the equipment's life expectancy.

Given that fact, we shuddered to think of the condition of previously-issued antidote and decontamination kits now in the hands of our military and emergency response personnel. Worse yet, we discovered that the various government agencies–like the Centers for Disease Control and Prevention (CDC), the Federal Emergency Management Agency (FEMA), and even the Red Cross–do not coordinate the wording used for civilians regarding Weapons of Mass Destruction, Natural Disasters, etc. Surprisingly, much of the data and information supplied by their web sites are written by consultants, not their own staffs. Thus, we were unable to locate two sites on the same subject that provided the same or similar formats for the avoidance, protection, or treatment of WMD agent exposure.

The information or guidelines on these agencies' websites contains reams of information that is useless for the average civilian, and we seriously doubt that even the Emergency Defense Preparedness Planners (mostly firemen and policemen in small cities and communities) have the time to read the volumes of information dumped onto those sites. For instance, under FEMA's "WMD Guidebook for Civilians," there are 58 pages of print for the Chemical portion, 36 pages for the Radiological portion, and 21 pages for the Biological portion.

We know that unless this is your hobby, or you are involved in the preparation of NBC/WMD documents, no one will read this mass of information, although we did—and we were astounded and dismayed at both its volume and its uselessness. Most other sites are similar in length and provide little or no useful knowledge for civilians regarding treatments or alternative medications, which should have been the main reason to write most of the papers.

We might be mistaken, but we were of the belief that the ONLY purpose of the military and civilians in the Emergency Response Groups is to protect the American citizenry, not just themselves! Yet practically all manuals, instructions, and guidelines are written for the most part to provide instructions and guidelines to military, emergency, and medical personnel. This is why we decided to write our own document for our own families.

"Justifications" for Not Informing or Providing Viable Information to the Public

During our research, we questioned numerous experts and many others as to why American citizens do not have sufficient medications, protective gear, or information in case of a WMD incident. The replies were of questionable logic and are often meant to keep the public completely dependent on these governmental agencies, rather than ensuring for the protection of the general public.

When we asked why civilians cannot purchase a complete WMD kit and protective clothing, we were told that it would be too costly to provide for everyone. The poor would be left out, and it could cause a panic if implemented. Our response is that Iraq purchased large quantities of Atropine (a nerve agent antidote, which our public cannot purchase here without a doctor's prescription) from Turkey, and Israel recently purchased large quantities of new gas masks and protective clothing for their citizenry.

It is true that our government can ill afford to purchase 280 million items for all Americans, but isn't it more sensible and rational to allow those wishing protection for themselves and their families to do so? Isn't this the essence of our American system of self-governance?

After all, if many have protection, it would cause less work, time, and effort for the emergency personnel that would be caring for others. It's also true that many of our poor would not use the money that they now spend on drugs, alcohol, and gambling to purchase safety and protective equipment and WMD kits. After all, the hope is the items will never be needed. But shouldn't all Americans be able to spend their income on the safety of their families, even if others make other choices?

Another reply was that a terrorist might obtain the items for evil purposes. The truth is that most policemen and emergency personnel infrequently practice with the limited quantities of equipment available, and if a terrorist is planning to kill hundreds or thousands, then obtaining this type of equipment will not be a problem. Also, terrorists are suicidal in nature and practice–they generally don't care about having protection for themselves since they expect to die anyway.

When we asked why our children are not taught what to do in the event of a WMD incident as we were in the 1950s, we were that told it would panic the communities and there isn't any equipment and kits for children. But just whom are we trying to protect? Why not make equipment and kits for infants, children, pregnant women, older people, etc.?

The U.S. could purchase medications, antidotes, and safety and protective equipment from foreign countries, thus keeping the production lines open and causing the prices to drop to reasonable levels. Granted, they would not be FDA-approved, but why couldn't we send our American inspectors to these foreign factories to ensure they are safe and properly made through testing and inspections? Or even have the foreign-manufactured items re-inspected at our FDA-approved facilities here in the USA, before being made available to American citizens?

It makes little sense that our factories cannot supply the needed quantities of medications and safety and protective equipment, particularly when our nation is in danger of attack at any moment. Tediously re-writing the same information has created jobs for many consultants in this field, but it does little to actually protect our citizenry.

Perhaps the worst part of this system are the petty bureaucrats who believe that only through hiding and limiting information to the public, will they be able to maintain their authority and retain their secure government positions. For the most part, these are the people who thwart the efforts to change the status quo, thus endangering the lives of all in our nation.

Experts in the field of Medicine and professionals in the fields Weapons of Mass Destruction (WMD) do not all agree on the proper procedures, medications, doses, practices, or even when or how mediations and treatments are to be administered. Thus, there are bound to be some, who will disagree with the information provided in this part of the book. My co-author and I accept all responsibility for any errors or omissions in this WMD safety and protection measure and treatments in this section of the book.

However, after we completed our research and the writing of the WMD guide, we sent copies of it to all of the U.S. government agencies associated with these subjects and issues for their review and correction:

- The Centers for Disease Control (CDC)

- The Federal Emergency Management Agency (FEMA)

- The Assistant Secretary of Defense for Biological and Chemical Defense

- Home Security (The Army Medical Branch)

- The Department of Energy.

Every agency, without exception, failed to even acknowledge receiving the document, never mind providing any needed corrections or suggestions. Thus, the information that we have compiled and presented herein is based on the list of documents and books provided in the Appendix. As of the initial publication of our guide on the Internet (August 2003), we had received no acknowledgement of it's receipt and even as of this writing, we are still awaiting replies from these agencies. Draw your own conclusions.

Final Thoughts

Since most people are untrained in these matters, we encourage you to review this information and determine what you and your family would plan to do in case of an accidental or intentional release of WMD agents. You might find that you will be on your own from one to ten days, and you should consider what actions you might want to take in order to protect yourself and your family members.

We have spent a lot of time and effort in compiling this data and hope you will take the time to read and discuss it with your family members. We also ask that our readers double check this our information with their doctors, or others whom you may know who have professional knowledge of these subjects, as they may view our suggestions from different viewpoints and have more up-to-date information.

We did the best we could do for all Americans and other world citizens, and hope that if the government fails or is unable to assist you in a time of crisis that the information enclosed will be of some use to all of you.

Again, we hope it will never be needed. We encourage those of you who believe you won't be near an epidemic center to reconsider. Accidental discharges from nuclear plants can spread radiation far and wide across a number of states. Similarly, people who travel outside your local areas can return with contagious diseases, which could infect entire communities. Equally important, terrorists have vowed to use any and all weapons of mass destruction to destroy our society and our way of life. Some people may not think them capable of carrying out such attacks, but we know they are - and the news is filled weekly with stories about such plans.

Major Frank C. Stolz, USMC (Ret.), Round Rock, TX

CWO-4 James E. Mulloy, USMC (Ret.), Oceanside, CA

December, 2004

www.WMDTerror.com

Chapter 1 – Atomic/Nuclear Radiation Incident Guidance

Understanding Radiation Exposure

Radiation is a form of energy that comes from a variety of sources: from man-made sources such as x-ray machines, from the sun and outer space, and from some natural materials such as uranium in the soil. Small quantities of radioactive materials occur naturally in the air we breathe, the water we drink, the food we eat, and even in our own bodies.

Most people's first major concern is about exposure to atomic or nuclear radiation fallout and contamination - to external contamination. But since what actually happens during an atomic/nuclear air blast, surface blast, or subsurface blast is irrelevant once it has occurred, you need the information about what to do in the event of such an exposure before an actual radiation incident occurs.

Radiation doses that people receive are measured in units called "*rem*" and "*sievert*" (one sievert is equal to 100 rem). Scientists estimate that the average person in the United States receives a dose of about one-third of a rem per year. Eighty percent of typical human exposure comes from natural sources, and 20% comes from artificial radiation sources, primarily medical X-rays.

Internal Radiation

Radiation that goes inside our bodies causes what we refer to as internal exposure or contamination. Internal contamination can occur in a variety of ways: the thyroid gland may accumulate higher doses of internal radiation after an atomic or nuclear blast, through breathing in radiated particles, or through eating foods, drinking liquids or ingesting medications that have been exposed to the effects of high radiation doses.

Recommended Treatment

Fortunately, Potassium Iodine (KI) is available now at most health food stores under the brand name RADON; it has a five-year shelf life and does not require a doctor's prescription. This product was recommended for the victims of the Three Mile Island (Pennsylvania) and Chernobyl (Russia) accidental nuclear waste discharges.

Unfortunately, this product provides protection ONLY for ingested radioactive iodine (RAI), which is often prescribed to treat hyperthyroidism (overactive thyroid) because of its simplicity: it is given in a single dose. RAI treatment is based on the fact that the thyroid actively accumulates iodine, which it uses to produce thyroid hormones required for normal body function.

This RAI is like the iodine found in foods such as fish, seaweed, and iodized salt, except that it releases an electron, or beta particle, that creates its therapeutic action. For use in treatment, RAI is taken dissolved in water or as a capsule. It is absorbed quickly by the stomach and intestines, and then carried in the bloodstream to the thyroid, where it is taken up by the gland.

While in the thyroid gland, the RAI disrupts the function of some of the thyroid cells: the more radioactive iodine given, the more cells cease to function. As the cells stop functioning, excessive amounts of thyroid hormones are no longer produced, and hyperthyroidism and other symptoms begin to disappear. (See Chapter 4 and the Appendix for additional NORAD Kit information.)

External radiation

As mentioned earlier, this type of exposure comes from radioactive sources outside your body, such as radiation from sunlight, man-made and naturally-occurring radioactive materials, as well as from atomic or nuclear radiation fallout and contamination. In a nuclear WMD situation, the body may be exposed to radiation as well as suffer burns, cuts, and even broken or missing limbs.

Recommended Treatment

NORAD does NOT protect from the damages of external radiation. When you are treating external radiation contamination, the problem is that radiation can be spread further on the victim or on yourself if proper care is not used. These are the minimal recommended practices (there is a more complete list starting on page 203):

1. Wash the area thoroughly with non-contaminated soap and water and keep under shelter if you are unable to leave the area.

2. Use protective clothing when you move and work on a victim or patient. Since this may be a near impossibility (as you probably won't have protective clothing), you will have to use whatever items you have available to protect yourself from

further contamination. For instance, a paint drop cloth or heavy raincoat, along with rubber boots, rubber gloves, and surgical masks can provide some protection to you and others from further radiation contamination.

3. If possible, wash the victim with clean water to remove radioactive dirt and debris before cleaning a wound, using clean gauze sponges or towelettes to further carefully clean the wound before bandaging and taping.

4. Seek medical attention for all victims as soon as possible

Health Effects of Radiation Exposure

Radiation affects the body in different ways, but the adverse health consequences of exposure may not be seen for many years. Adverse health effects range from mild contamination such as skin reddening, to serious effects such as cancer and death. These adverse health effects are determined by the amount of radiation absorbed by the body (the dose), the type of radiation, the route of exposure, and the length of time a person is exposed.

Acute radiation syndrome (ARS), or radiation sickness, is usually caused when a person receives a high dose of radiation to much of the body in a matter of minutes. Survivors of the Hiroshima and Nagasaki atomic bombs and firefighters responding to the Chernobyl nuclear power plant event in 1986 experienced ARS.

The cells that are most sensitive to radiation are those that line the intestine (crypt cells), the white blood cells that fight infection, and the cells that make red and white blood cells. The impact on these cells leads to the classic early symptoms of radiation sickness. For instance, damage to the intestinal cells causes nausea, vomiting, and dehydration. Radiation penetrates the body and is wholly or partially absorbed by soft and hard tissue. Radioactive fallout in the form of particulate matter can be swallowed and/or inhaled.

The immediate symptoms of ARS are nausea, vomiting, and diarrhea. Later, bone marrow depletion may lead to weight loss, loss of appetite, flu-like symptoms, infection, and bleeding. The survival rate depends on the radiation dose. For those who do survive, full recovery can take from a few weeks up to two years.

Children who are exposed to radiation may be more at risk than adults. Radiation exposure to the unborn child is of special concern because the human embryo or fetus is extremely sensitive to radiation.

Radiation exposure, like exposure to the sun, is cumulative.

Protecting Against Radiation Exposure

How to Reduce Radiation Exposure

The three basic ways to reduce radiation exposure are through:

1. **Time:** Decrease the amount of time you spend near the source of radiation.

2. **Distance:** The distance one is from the source of radiation is critical in reducing radiation exposure. Increase the distance between you and the radiation source as quickly as possible.

3. **Shielding:** Anything that creates a barrier between people and the radiation source. Being inside a building or a vehicle can provide shielding from some forms of radiation.

4. **Increasing the shielding between you and the radiation source:** Depending on the type of radiation, the shielding can range from something as thin as a plate of window glass, or as thick as several feet of concrete, such as a building.

Recognizing Radiation Sickness Symptoms

There are many symptoms of radiation sickness, and their severity varies greatly depending on the dosage.

Initial symptoms

Initial symptoms may include: nausea, vomiting, diarrhea and fatigue.

Secondary symptoms

Secondary symptoms may include:

- Headache
- Rapid heartbeat
- Worsening of tooth or gum disease
- Dry cough
- Burning, permanent skin darkening
- Hemorrhage

- Shortness of breath
- Inflammation of the mouth and throat
- Hair loss
- Heart inflammation with chest pain
- Bleeding spots anywhere under the skin
- Anemia.

In severe anemia cases where the radiation exposure has been high, death may occur within two to four weeks. Those who survive six weeks after receiving a single large dose of radiation to the whole body may generally be expected to recover.

Treating Acute Radiation Sickness (ARS)

You can use anti-nausea drugs and painkillers to relieve symptoms of radiation sickness. Antibiotics may also be needed to fight off secondary infection. Blood transfusions may be necessary for patients suffering from anemia. See Chapter 4 for more information on treatments and remedies readily available to the public.

Immediate Action to Take During an Atomic/ Nuclear Incident

1. Get down on the ground or floor, and cover your eyes from the bright flash to avoid being blinded.

2. Get under a desk, table, tree, car or any covering to protect from flying glass and debris. Remain in this position until the heat wave passes over and debris stops flying about.

3. Locate and organize survivors – family members and others– in order to assist one another using these procedures:

4. Cover your faces with a wet cloth to avoid breathing radioactive dust. Wipe all exposed skin with a damp cloth, including under nails. Avoid using contaminated water!

5. If possible, try to determine the distance from the center of the blast, as you may not be contaminated if you are far enough away and upwind from the blast center.

6. Find a radio to hear the news of the incident, and obtain guidance from authorities.

7. Call authorities or medical personnel for further guidance, if possible.

8. If you are at home or with family members, locate your NORAD (KI) Kit. Use it only if you are certain that what happened was, in fact, an atomic or nuclear blast, and have been told to do so by authorities.

9. Locate and store or re-store canned foods, and uncontaminated water and other liquids.

10. Determine through authorities which foods and liquids might remain uncontaminated. Check all food for any possible chances of contamination, such as discoloration, being unwrapped or in an open condition, where contamination is possible. In the case of drink sources – water or other liquids – look for any that have been open to the elements or to the radiation fallout. You should be able to see discoloration or sense a minimal change in taste. The best solution is to move as far away from known contaminated areas as possible before you use any food or liquid products that might have become contaminated in any manner.

11. If possible, shower and wash thoroughly with non-contaminated soap and water in order to decontaminate your person, if you were near a radiation fallout area.

12. If you are within 10 miles of the blast center, replace the clothing you are wearing if possible with uncontaminated clothing. Place the used clothing in a plastic bag or container. If you are unable to change, shake out your clothing so the dust blows away from you and others around you (downwind).

13. Be armed and prepared to defend yourself and your family, as people who panic or are crazed will do all they can to take what you have in order to protect themselves.

14. Soon after the incident, the area will likely be filled with emergency personnel trying to enter the area, while simultaneously other civilians are trying to flee, so avoid the normally heavily traveled roads whenever possible.

15. Since you most likely are not emergency workers or medically trained, it is best for you to get out of the immediate blast area, as you are more apt to hinder trained personnel than to help them.

16. If possible, try to leave the area surrounding the blast area, and take food, clothing, medications, guns, ammunition, and the NORAD kit with you.

17. DO NOT waste time trying to save valuables, photos, pets, etc. Get yourself and your family out of the area as soon as you can as you are now strictly in a survival mode.

18. Contact relatives and friends once you are outside of the incident area and in another location far away from the blast location.

19. Once you are safely in a non-contaminated town or city, seek medical assistance and advice as soon as possible.

When You Cannot Leave the Area

If you are stuck in a contaminated radiated area and cannot move yourself or family members, follow these steps after taking the above steps.

1. Dig an underground shelter and cover yourself with six or more inches of topsoil and to remain covered until you are informed it is safe to emerge. While this may not appear to be the best solution for many, walking around in known contaminated spaces will more than likely stir up more radiated dust particles, which unnecessarily exposes you and others to even more radiation doses.

   Some protection is better than none at all. Remember that everything, from glass to canvas tarps and doors, and even clothing, affords some protection from the various forms of radiation, so anything between you and the radiation limits the amount of the dose you might receive.

2. Seek medical attention as soon as practical.

3. Bury contaminated food, liquids and clothing to avoid recontamination, if you must remain in the area.

Sources of Information on Radiation

Within the Executive Branch of the Federal Government, there are several Executive Departments and independent agencies whose counter-terrorism programs provide information about radiation and its risks:

- The Nuclear Regulatory Commission Radiation Protection and Emergency Response Program (Independent Agency)
  (301) 415-8200
  www.nrc.gov/what-we-do/radiation.html

- The Federal Emergency Management Agency (FEMA) in the Dept. of Homeland Security (DHS)
  (202) 646-4600
  www.fema.gov

- The Radiation Emergency Assistance Center/Training Site (REAC/TS) in the Dept. of Energy (DOE)
  (865) 576-3131 (ask for REAC/TS)
  www.orau.gov/reacts/intro.htm

- The U.S. National Response Team, an interagency group co-chaired by the EPA (Independent Agency) and the U.S. Coast Guard
  1-800-dial-DOE
  www.epa.gov/superfund/programs/er/nrs/nrsnrt.htm

- Find your State Radiation Control Director by contacting the Conference of Radiation Control Program Directors (CRCPD), a nonprofit organization of individuals that regulate and control the use of radioactive material and radiation sources.
  (502) 227-4543
  www.crcpd.org

Chapter 2 – Chemical Incident Guidance

Introduction

While contamination of chemical agents can include everything from toxic spills of radioactive materials to pesticides, and from toxic chemical discharges in waterways to accidental spillage of chemicals such as Chlorine, Phosgene, etc., we will concentrate on those we are most likely to encounter via aerosol devices, which are the most likely method of attack by terrorists.

Chemical Agent Categories

This section covers four major categories of chemical agents - what they are and some basic treatments:

- Nerve

- Blister

- Blood

- Choking

We will not address here categories such as incapacitating, vomiting, and irritant agents. The military and medical personnel have detector paper to detect and determine the type of chemical agents used, along with gas masks, protective clothing, and antidote, decontamination, and protection kits, but the general American public has none of these.

Perhaps the one "good" thing about these chemical agents is that many can be removed with soap and water, and a wet cloth over the face can prevent inhaling much of the gases or vapors.

Please see Chapter 4 for more information on surgical gas masks and where to order them.

Nerve Gases or Agents

Nerve Agents are chemicals that interfere with the Central Nervous System. Upon exposure to these agents, the body's muscles tightly contract and cannot relax, then the muscles contract at an accelerated rate.

Nerve agents you are most likely to encounter:

- GA-Tabon

- GB-Sarin

- GD Soman

- VX

Characteristics of Nerve Gases or Agents

	GA-Tabon	GB-Sarin	GD-Soman	VX
Appearance	Colorless or brownish.	Colorless.	Colorless.	Colorless
Odor	None.	None.	Fruity, impurities give it the odor of camphor.	None.
Persistency	Heavily coated with liquid can last two days; evaporates 20 times slower than water.	Heavily coated with liquid can last two days; evaporates 20 times slower than water.	Heavily coated with liquid can last two days; evaporates 20 times slower than water.	A refined version of Tabon and Sarin. A highly toxic and persistent substance that can be present in both a liquid and vaporous state.
Rate of Action	Very rapid, can cause death 15 minutes after a heavy dose heavy dose	Very rapid, can cause death 15 minutes after a heavy dose heavy dose	Very rapid, can cause death 15 minutes after a heavy dose heavy dose	Can cause death minutes after exposure It can enter the body by inhalation, ingestion, through the eyes and skin. Absorbed into the human body and attacks the central nervous system before

	GA-Tabon	GB-Sarin	GD-Soman	VX
				attacking the lungs and heart.
				Considered at least 100 times more toxic by entry through the skin than the nerve agent Sarin, and twice as toxic by inhalation.

Symptoms of Nerve Gases or Agents

The severity of symptoms varies and depends on how the agent enters the body.

- **Eyes:** Symptoms appear fast, within 2 to 3 minutes and can cause death in 1 to 10 minutes.

- **Respiratory System:** Symptoms appear in 2-5 minutes and can cause death in 1 to 10 minutes.

- **Skin:** Symptoms appear more slowly; heavy coatings can cause death in 1 to 2 hours; very small dosages sometimes cause local sweating and tremors with little other effects.

Mild symptoms of nerve agent poisoning	**Severe symptoms of nerve agent poisoning**
• Runny nose	• Strange or confused

- Drooling

- Sweating and muscle twitching in area of contamination

- Nausea

- Sudden headache

- Blurred Vision

- Stomach cramps

- Convulsions

behavior

- Eye pupils very small

- Vomiting

- Involuntary urination or defecation

- Unconsciousness.

- Wheezing and difficulty breathing

- Red eyes and tears

- Muscles twitching and weak feeling

Protection from and treatment of Nerve Gases or Agents

- Cover the body to protect from contact with agent droplets.

- Use a gas mask if available, or cover face with damp cloth if time permits.

- Flush any exposed skin with water or any liquid available as soon as possible.

- Use *Atropine*, a nerve agent antidote, or *Pralidoxime (Protopam)*, which is presently unavailable to the general public in the USA without prescription, but we have heard it can be purchased over-the-counter in Mexico and in other countries. However, you must insure the items are tamper proof, as you might end up purchasing medications that are diluted or of questionable consistency.

Blister Agents

Common blister agents or mustard gases you are most likely encounter:

- H (Levinstein Mustard)

- HD (Distilled Mustard)

- HN (Nitrogen Mustard)

- HT (Mustard Mixture)

- HL (Mustard-Lewisite Mixture)

Less common blister agents with which you should be familiar:

- L (Lewisite)

- PD (Phenyldichloroarsine)

- ED (Ethyldichloroarsine)

- MD (Methyldichloroarsine)

- CX (Phosgene Oxide)

Characteristics of Blister Agents

- **Appearance:** Can be oily or liquid, and the color can range from colorless to amber, pale yellow to a very dark liquid.

- **Odor:** Can smell like garlic, fruity, musty, geraniums, or even odorless if the agent is pure.

- **Persistency:** Depends on the amount of dose, the victim's health, and your ability to leave contaminated areas. Health problems can last from weeks to years.

- **Rate of Action:** Blisters normally appear in 4 to 12 hours.

Protection from and treatment of Blister Agents

There is no direct treatment for exposure to sulfur mustards or other blistering agents. The primary recommended treatment is to clean and disinfect the wounds produced by this agent.

- Immediately wash any part of your body exposed to agent.

- Flush your eyes with water only.

- Cover any blisters with sterile bandage.

- Never break the blisters.

- Wash down areas you will be working in with water or steam, to ensure you don't touch more of the agent.

- Washing items with soda (sodium carbonate)

destroys Blister Agents, but it acts much slower than bleach or caustic soda, and it should never be used on people.

- Caustic soda (lye) with water will decontaminate Lewisite from things, but don't use it on people.

- Ignited fuels can be used in safe areas to destroy Blister Agents by burning, while solvents merely tend to dilute them.

Blood Chemical Agents (Chemical Asphyxiates)

Blood agents that contain cyanides interfere with the body's ability to process oxygen. Small amounts cause little or no effect; however, high concentrations are very lethal. Other blood agents, like arsine, can cause damage to the organs.

Types of blood agents you are most likely to encounter:

- AC (Hydrogen Cyanide)

- CK (Cyanogens Chloride)

- SA (Arsine)

Characteristics of Blood Chemical Agents

- **Appearance:** AC and CK are a colorless liquid, or gaseous, while SA is a colorless gas.

- **Odor:** AC has an almond-like smell and very faint, while CK is very pungent and may go unnoticed because of tearing eyes and possible choking sensation. SA has a mild garlic odor.

- **Persistency:** All three are of short duration due to quick dissipation into the air.

- **Rate of Action:** AC has a very rapid incapacitation within 1 to 2 minutes, and death occurs in about 15 minutes if dose is lethal. CK immediate intense irritation. SA has delayed effects from 2 hours to 11 days.

Symptoms of Blood Chemical Agents

- **Low concentrations** can cause convulsions that may last for several hours, and it also can cause irrationality, alters reflexes, and produce an unsteady gait that can last for weeks. Recovery is normally complete under low concentrations.

- **Moderate** concentrations cause dizziness and nausea, and headaches can occur very quickly. Skin, lips, and fingertips will have a pink color.

- **High concentrations** cause respiration problems within a few seconds, violent convulsions or coma occur within 20-30 seconds, and breathing stops within a few minutes.

Protection from and treatment of Blood Chemical Agents

The recommended method of protection is to use a gas mask or damp cloth to prevent inhaling the blood agents. The treatment is based on the dosage inhaled or entering the body through various avenues.

Today, there is no medical antidote against Hydrogen Cyanide (CA) poisoning. The recommended treatment includes: an *Amyl Nitrate Inhalant* for temporary treatment until an IV treatment is available, then *Sodium Nitrate IV*, next a *Sodium Thiosulfate IV*, and *Vitamin B-12*. As stated above, a high dosage can cause almost immediate death, while a moderate dose should be treated quickly by decontaminating with water. Move the victim from the contaminated area and keep the person walking to assist the body's own ability to excrete cyanide.

The treatment for CK (Cyanogens Chloride) is identical as that for Hydrogen Cyanide (CA), except the choking sensation may require the added treatment for Choking agents below. There is no known antidote for Arsine (SA); however, the treatments include injecting IV fluids to flush out the agent and using blood transfusions to cleanse the blood of the agent.

Standard Choking Agents

Most common choking agents you are likely to encounter:

- CG (Phosgene)

- DP (Diphosgene)

Characteristics of Standard Choking Agents

	CG (Phosgene)	DP (Diphosgene)
Appearance	A colorless gas.	A colorless liquid.
Odor	Like new mown hay.	Like new mown hay.
Persistency	Short, but it depends on wind movements.	30 minutes to 3 hours when the weather is warm, and can remain for 10 to 12 hours when cold.
Rate of Action	2 to 3 hours, sometimes longer.	3 hours or longer.

Symptoms of Standard Choking Agents

- Coughing
- Tightness in the chest
- Tearing of the eyes

- Choking
- Headache
- Nausea
- Occasional vomiting

Protection from and treatment of Standard Choking Agents

Use a gas mask or damp cloth over the nose and mouth for protection, and if possible, have the victim sit up, rest, keep warm, and remain upright - *DO NOT LET THE VICTIM LIE FLAT.* Generally speaking, if a patient can rest and survive until the danger of pulmonary edema (fluids filling the lungs) is past, the person has a good chance of full recovery.

Chapter 3 – Biological (Germ)
Incident Guidance

Introduction

Atomic/nuclear and chemical attacks call for immediate actions to prevent further contamination and exposure.

This chapter deals with biological (germ) attacks. While there are some immediate actions that can be taken during a Biological Agent release, initial casualties usually have time to be treated both before and during the incubation period. However, as the disease spreads, the casualty figures can overwhelm support services, and supplies of medications can swiftly be depleted. Therefore, this section will include not only CDC-preferred medications and treatments, but also lists of optional alternatives, in case medical assistance and/or medication are unavailable.

There is always the possibility that several agents can be mixed or new strains developed. That situation means it could take medical specialists longer periods of time to determine the specific agents involved and the preferred treatment. Therefore, maintaining your health through optional and alternative medications might improve your survivability possibilities.

There are far too many biological agents to properly address here, and that is not the intent of this document. Rather, we will list emergency treatments and medications for those agents deemed most likely to be encountered during an accidental or intentional biological agent release.

It goes without saying that doctors or medical personnel should be consulted before using or recommending any medications to anyone. The wrong dosages can prove more devastating than the lack of applying any medications.

We strongly recommend that medical personnel, as well as your own doctors, review this information to insure that any of the suggested medications will not cause more harm than good. For instance, diabetes medication may prove fatal or debilitating if used with some of the suggested or alternative medications listed.

The same precautions should be taken for using any of the radiation, biological, or chemical agent remedies listed or suggested in this document.

Our main concern is with the most contagious and harmful biological agents; therefore, we will address what we believe are the most important.

Since the antidotes, remedies, and treatments for each biological agent are unique, this section will not follow the same format as that used for chemical exposures.

About Bacteria and Viruses

The release of small clouds of bacteria or viruses could easily and silently infect numerous people. Initially, the victims may have no signs of the infection and could thus spread the infections to others without knowing it. The infections can cause death if not treated appropriately.

Not all bacteria are bad. In fact, some types are required to sustain life in plants, animals, and humans, but some can also cause death. Viruses, on the other hand, are usually bad; they cause infectious diseases and can cause death.

Some Medical Terms to Understand

- The term *pathogen* means that a specific biological (transmitter) agent (either a virus or bacteria) has been identified.

- If you are notified that a *biological agent (virus or bacteria)* has been accidentally or purposely released in your location, DO NOT PANIC, as there are differing incubation periods for each type of bacteria or virus.

- *Antibiotics* are a substance or semi-synthetic substance derived from a microorganisms that, in a dilute solution, are able to inhibit or kill other microorganisms.

- *Antitoxin* is an antibody capable of neutralizing a specific toxin (poison) agent. It is often in the form of a serum and is used to counteract toxin agents.

- *Antidote* is a remedy to counteract the effects of a poison. It can be a remedy that might relieve, prevent, or counteract a toxic agent.

- *Infectious diseases* can be spread long after the initial attack or exposure through coughing, sneezing, or being in close contact with infected people. Smallpox, a deadly disease, is often spread in this manner.

Biological Agents

Smallpox Virus

Smallpox was thought to have been eradicated in 1979. However, strains have been stored by several nations in their laboratories, and this virulent disease is thought to still be available for use by biological terrorist groups. Whether spread intentionally or accidentally, it is one of the fastest-spreading and deadliest diseases known to medical specialists.

Smallpox is a 30% fatal disease if not treated, and there is a 97% survivability rate if the victim is inoculated within five days of exposure (exposure being considered being within six feet of an infected person for one hour). The so-called smallpox vaccine is a misnomer; it was produced originally from the Cow Pox virus vaccine. This vaccine is now called a *vaccinia*, which was found to produce antibodies in our systems to fight off all similar pox viruses.

The vaccinia virus was eventually produced in the form of a needle vaccination, which produced a small sore in the vaccinated area, and this in turn caused the system's antibodies to attack all types of pox viruses. While the vaccinia virus vaccine is presently in short supply, efforts are underway to mass produce this vaccine.

The vaccine has now been taken out of the experimental drug category by the FDA and "can" be mass produced and made available. One person in a million can get ill from the vaccinia vaccine (there is a higher chance of being struck by lightning). Department of Defense (DoD) active duty personnel have top priority for the vaccine.

A smallpox vaccine is being tested by our military forces, emergency workers, and the President at the present time; however, this vaccine is not yet available to the general public in sufficient quantities for protection.

Public health plan for this vaccination and others

- **Prevention:** Vaccinate all Public Health and Emergency Responder personnel.

- **Outbreak (one or more cases):** Mass vaccination (all local population in the infected area) using the National Pharmaceutical Stockpile (two mobile and loaded 747s are kept full of drugs ready to deliver in shot doses). Each County Emergency Services and Public Health Dept. either has, or is in the process of developing, a reception/security/media and distribution plan to address this issue.

  Note: Those who had old smallpox vaccinations when they were children are NOT considered currently vaccinated. In fact, it takes more vaccine to inoculate them than an un-vaccinated individual due to possible resistance in the system from the previous vaccination. There is some good news: the smallpox virus can be killed with simple household bleaches, should you drop a vial during the inoculation process or accidentally contaminate yourself.

Smallpox agent release notification

- Determine if you or your family members are in the target area, and find out if vaccines are planned for your location.

- Get out of the area immediately, if possible, to prevent contamination or further contamination of you and your family members.

- *Cidofovir* is now being considered as a potential therapy, but it is not yet accepted as a proven treatment.

- Standard disinfectants are effective on surfaces, and hot water and bleach are necessary for exposed clothing and linens.

- Alternative medications (if *Cidofovir* or *vaccinia* virus vaccines are unavailable) include *Variolinum, Vaccinotoxinum,* and *Vaccininum,* which are Nosodes[2] (see Chapter 4, Home Remedies, for more about Nosode products). These are 19th and 20th century remedies for smallpox, and they were found to work on infected patients and prevent the spread of the disease. Thus, if/when emergency workers run out of supplies or are unavailable, you have some alternative means for self-protection if you have stocked up in advance.

---

[2] Nosodes are a particular type of homeopathic remedy used primarily for food poisoning.

Anthrax (Bacillus Anthraces)

Anthrax is a hardy biological threat that is resistant to sunlight, heat, and disinfectants. Although it is a naturally-occurring disease found in grazing animals, immunizations of domestic animals have all but eliminated anthrax among farm-bred animals.

Anthrax can be produced as very small, dry spores that are durable and easy to spread. An aerosol cloud would be colorless, odorless, and invisible. The good news is that anthrax is not contagious; the bad news is there are three ways to become infected with the anthrax disease.

Means of infection

The first way is by having a person with cuts or lesions and come in contact with an anthrax-infected animal. This form of anthrax is rarely fatal if treated soon after the spider bite-appearing infection appears. It takes days to turn into a sore with a black center of dead tissue (incubation period is normally one to five days).

The second method of infection is through the digestive system by eating infected meat, although this form of transfer of the disease has proven to be an infrequent occurrence. This infection is characterized by inflammation of the intestinal tract, nausea and loss of appetite that is later followed by bloody vomiting and severe diarrhea. If left untreated, death results in 25% to 60% of cases (incubation period one to three days).

The third and worst method is via inhalation of the spores, as from an aerosol cloud or vapor release. If left untreated, death can result in 95% of cases. The time period for symptoms to appear is similar to those above and depends on the number of spores/bacteria inhaled, eaten, or transferred to the body. The spores reach the lungs and migrate to the lymph nodes, where they change into a bacterial form, multiply and produce toxins. The disease is hard to diagnose, as its symptom are like influenza.

There are two phases to this disease:

- The first is a flu-like syndrome with low grade fever, headache, muscle aches, etc. Improvement occurs after several days, and then the second phase kicks in.

- Phase 2 usually begins with acute respiratory distress leading to respiratory failure.

Symptoms of Anthrax

The symptoms include fever, enlarged lymph nodes in the neck, and difficulty breathing. Low blood pressure, chills, and rapid deterioration lead to shock and eventually to coma occur around the seventh day. Death usually occurs within 24-36 hours of this secondary phase (the incubation period is one to six days).

Treatment of Anthrax

Since we are primarily concerned with an accidental or intentional release of aerosol anthrax, we need to concentrate on the remedy for this form of infection. The FDA method recommended as the first line of defense is the antibiotic *Ciprofloxacin* or *Cipro*.

Pregnant women and children are recommended to use penicillin unless they are allergic to it. Other forms of antibiotics available as alternatives to anthrax are: *Penicillin, Erythromycin, Chloramhenicol, Doxycycline, Streptomycin,* and *Tetracycline.*

Note that a vaccine for inhaled anthrax is presently being tested on our military and emergency worker personnel; however, the results are unclear and are not currently available to the general public.

An alternative Nosode is *Anthracnum,* although its usefulness for inhaled anthrax is currently unknown. Also, an herb called *Echinacea* has been used as an anthrax remedy, but not for inhaled anthrax.

Botulism (Clostridium Botulinum)

Botulism is a severe type of bacterial food poisoning that is considered a real terrorist threat due to its ease of introduction into the food supply and the high death rate that can occur if it is left untreated. Foods may not appear contaminated, but even a small amount ingested can cause a full-blown case of the disease.

Almost every type of food that is not very acidic can support botulism bacterial growth and toxin production. One of the best ways to destroy most of the seven standard types of bacteria is through irradiation, using electrical beams, which change the molecules in the pathogens and kill the toxic bacteria. The FDA recently allowed this form of irradiation to be used on meals for school children; it is also used to destroy anthrax spores.

Means of infection

Discard any canned foods showing evidence of spoilage, leakages, or swelling.

Variations of this bacteria can be found in meats, sea foods, vegetables, fruits, oils, potatoes, etc., so there is a need for care in food preparation, handling, and storage.

The bacteria's spores are highly heat-resistant and may survive boiling for several hours at 212°F, but they are less resistant to moist heat at 248°F for 30 minutes. Toxin production can also occur in refrigerated temperatures as low as 37°F, as these organisms do not require strict oxygen-free conditions.

Symptoms of Botulism

Botulism primarily affects the nervous system and the onset is often abrupt, occurring as soon as two hours or eight days after eating contaminated food. Early signs are: weakness, dizziness, possible double vision, and difficulty in speaking and swallowing.

Other symptoms may be vomiting, diarrhea, and abdominal cramps.

Major symptoms can include respiratory failure caused by paralysis. Symptoms for small children or infants may begin as constipation or diarrhea that should be treated by medical personnel.

Treatment of Botulism

An antitoxin is presently being tested for five of the seven known types of Botulism.

The standard treatment is an antitoxin like ***Connaught Trivalent Botulinal***.

Plague (Bubonic and Pneumonic)

As we all know from our history books, the Black Plague was spread across Europe by rats that in turn carried the plague-infected fleas to their human hosts. However, the probability of flea carriers is rather remote in today's society, and the probability is that release of these plagues would more likely be in the form of bacteria or aerosol sprays.

There are two types of plague:

- Bubonic
- Pneumonic.

Bubonic plague

This strain has a normal incubation period of from one to six days after infection and can vary from three hours to twelve days.

Symptoms of Bubonic plague

The symptoms are chills and fever up to 106°F, and the victim usually shows a rapid pulse coupled with low blood pressure.

Other symptoms are enlarged tender lymph nodes, poor circulation in the hands and feet, and persistent cold, blue, and sweaty digits. Lesions often appear at the site of infections caused by a bite; however, an aerosol spray would not provide for a bite location.

Treatment of Bubonic plague

If treated in the early stages, the recovery rate from this is very good; however, this can be a communicable disease. In that case, surgical masks or other precautions are necessary when treating a victim of this disease, and a vaccine is also helpful for protection.

The treatment for Bubonic Plague is the common antibiotic *Tetracycline*, although a more severe form of Bubonic Plague called Septicemia Plague requires *Streptomycin* as a treatment.

Pneumonic plague

This is the least common of the two, and accounts for only about 2% of recorded cases. However, this makes it an ideal weapon because there is no real effective vaccine at the present time. This strain is highly infectious; surgical masks and other precautions are necessary when treating victims.

Symptoms of Pneumonic plague

Its symptoms are similar to those above for Bubonic Plague, followed by shortness of breath, severe weakness, a cough showing specks of blood, and finally pneumonia.

Treatment of Pneumonic plague

If treated within 24 hours, the chances of recovery are much higher. The treatment for this disease is *Streptomycin*, and the alternatives are ***Gentamicin, Oral Doxycycline***, and ***Fluoroquinolones***. Antibiotics are an effective treatment if they are dispensed properly and in a timely manner.

Other Viruses

We considered including some of the more familiar viruses such as ***Ebola*** (a virus originally found in Africa, and thought to derive from monkey or chimpanzee and human contact, as well as through infected blood or human secretions to other humans). We also considered including ***Legionnaires Disease (Legionella)***, which is believed to be the result of experiments with a non-lethal germ that turned into a killer bacteria in Russia. How it got into the hotel's water system is unknown, but the vapors from the cooling system infected about 200 people at a convention in a Philadelphia hotel and led to the deaths of around 30 Legionnaires.

There are numerous other viruses, bacteria, and diseases that we could have addressed, but this is intended to be a "quick and dirty" WMD survival document, not a comprehensive medical remedy guide for all possible illnesses and potential remedies.

We recommend reviewing our reading and resource list (Appendix) to anyone who is seriously interested in further information on this subject. Many will find it boring, but the information is important if you are serious about educating yourself on WMD protective issues.

Chapter 4 – Home Remedies

Introduction

The home remedies and equipment described in this section can be used without a doctor's prescription. They are mentioned as appropriate under each section for treating Nuclear/Biological/Chemical (NBC) injuries. You should always consult with a licensed Health Practitioner, Naturopathic Physician, or Homeopathic Practitioner (who are more sympathetic to these types of treatments than most allopathic physicians) for use and doses, etc., before using alternative medications.

Home Remedy Treatments and Considerations

Homeopathic medications

"Homeopathy is a system of medicine that is based on the Law of Similars. ... Samuel Hahnemann described this principle by using a Latin phrase: *Similia Similibus Curentur*, which translates: 'Let likes cure likes.' It is a principle that has been known for centuries. Hahnemann developed the principle into a system of medicine called homeopathy, and it has been used successfully for the last 200 years, including still by the British Royal Family." (From the website of the National Center for Homeopathy – See the Appendix for more about this resource.)

Homeopathic treatments and considerations

Homeopathic medications have usually been opposed by orthodox medical practitioners, but their use has increased in popularity due to dissatisfaction with standard medical practices.

As we are all aware, home remedy medications were used by many in the past when medical assistance was impractical or too costly, and these medications include Nosodes and other remedies used primarily for food poisoning.

Nosodes are a particular type of homeopathic remedy made from a diseased product. They are used primarily to treat food poisoning. (These remedies are listed under the Biological Agents section [Smallpox and Botulism] in Chapter 3.)

These remedies are made from dilutions of pathological organs or tissues, or weakened bacteria, fungi, parasites, viruses, or yeasts and are used selectively to assist the body to eliminate a disease without adding any byproducts such as those found in vaccines. Nosodes are believed to stimulate the immune system. They might be used after exposure to a given agent and might prevent or limit development of the disease.

Our logic is that something is better than nothing. Nosodes are also thought to be safe for children, infants, pregnant women, and the elderly; however, checking with your own physician, pharmacist or naturopathic doctor for safety and use should be your first step if you ever consider using this form of home medication.

Holistic medications

"Holistic medicine is the art and science of healing that addresses the whole person - body, mind, and spirit. The practice of holistic medicine integrates conventional and alternative therapies to prevent and treat disease, and most importantly, to promote optimal health. This condition of holistic health is defined as the unlimited and unimpeded free flow of life force energy through body, mind, and spirit.

Holistic medicine encompasses all safe and appropriate modalities of diagnosis and treatment. It includes analysis of physical, nutritional, environmental, emotional, spiritual and lifestyle elements. Holistic medicine focuses upon patient education and participation in the healing process." (From the website of the American Holistic Medical Association – see the Appendix for more about this resource.)

Holistic treatments include a wide range of cures from minerals and oils to vitamins. These are used primarily to maintain and strengthen the immune system and to fight off bacteria and viruses. Some of these treatments are listed below.

Holistic treatments and considerations

As with herbs, don't expect these types of medical alternatives to produce immediate results. Nearly all require frequent and sustained use to be of any health value. Use of any treatments should be under the supervision of medical personnel if possible, and in our opinion should be a last option, when nothing else is available. Please check with your doctor and an Herbalist to determine proper dosages.

Much more information is available in these two books: The Way of Herbs and Natural Defenses Against Bioterrorism (fully listed in the Appendix). All possible herbs and alternative medications for these conditions are not listed, as there are far too many to list. These are simply those we thought most useful for your consideration for these circumstances.

- **Beta Glucan:** Increases ability of immune cells to destroy bacterial, viral, and fungal organisms.

- **Calcium D-Glucarate:** Limits toxins produced by pathogen bacteria from reabsorbing into body.

- **Chlorella:** An algae from freshwater sources containing chlorophyll, which fights bacteria and viruses by increasing white blood cell activity

- **Chlorinated water:** One of the best defenses against microbes (germs), as it kills most of them, and it would take massive numbers of diseased microbes to cause massive casualties. Additionally, boiling water for extended periods of time kills many of any remaining bacteria or microbes.

- **Colloidal Silver:** An antibacterial agent used in water filters.

- **Minerals:** Zinc, manganese, selenium, etc., help maintain the immune system, and have antioxidant properties. Too much of any minerals can prove to be harmful.

- **Vinegar:** A powerful antiseptic, especially

white vinegar. It kills dangerous bacteria on contact, such as some forms of Salmonella, which can cause food poisoning.

- **Vitamins:** Helpful to the immune system in different ways. For instance, Vitamins A, C, and E are essential in small quantities for nutrition. Vitamin A is found mainly in animal products (eggs, milk yolk, fish oil); lack of this vitamin can cause visual defects. Vitamin B12 is essential for blood formation, neural function, and growth. Vitamin C (ascorbic acid) prevents scurvy. There are variations of the same type of vitamin like B6, etc., and a doctor or pharmacist should be consulted on the uses and need for any vitamin supplements, although multi-vitamins are usually thought to be safe for the general public.

- **Water purification tablets**: Available in most camping and drug stores and good to have on hand for any given situation.

Herbal medications

Herbs are another form of natural medication used against a variety of microorganisms, for which pharmaceutical drugs may have proven to be impotent or ineffective. Like homeopathic and holistic medications or other remedies, herbs have taken on a greater importance with the emergence of antibiotic-resistant strains of bacteria. A list of herbs relating to the above concerns is provided below.

Herbal treatments and considerations

With the emergence of antibiotic-resistant strains of bacteria, natural products have taken on a greater importance in fighting diseases. These are not a panacea (cure- all), but simply an alternative if nothing is available or working, just like the holistic alternatives. It is important to know that nearly all of these herbs and holistic remedies usually require long and repeated usage to be of much use; therefore, you should not expect any of these to be miracle overnight cures. These substances are typically available in various forms at most natural foods and health food stores.

Many books are available through public libraries, health food stores and the Internet that describe how to prepare potions and preparations made of these substances.

- **Aloe Vera:** A dried, powdered form of this plant can be used for hepatitis, liver problems and constipation. The gel form can be used for burns and injuries. Many people grow the plant in their homes for decorative as well as medicinal purposes.

- **Aniseed:** Affects the stomach, lungs, liver, and kidney systems; used to treat intestinal gas, nausea, abdominal pains, coughs and colds.

- **Garlic:** Used in WW1 in many forms as an antibiotic with field dressings, because it possesses potent sulfur-containing anti-microbial and antiseptic properties.

- **Berberine with Goldenseal:** Used for intestinal disorders and purportedly to inhibit bacteria growth. Also, Berberine Sulfate is thought by herbalists to assist in reducing the stomach

239

bacteria for E. Coli, Shigellosis (bacteria causing dysentery), Vibrio (a class of bacteria), and Staphylococcus (a class of bacteria).

- **Black Walnut:** Used as an antiseptic, as well as to reduce Salmonella and E.Coli bacteria.

- **Bloodroot:** Reportedly used for skin cancer, gum disease, skin eruptions, coughs, and sore throats.

- **Boneset:** Used for fevers, colds, flu, and intestinal problems.

- **Old Man's Beard:** A type of lichen (a number of the lichens contain antibiotic properties); in some cases, some have been reported to be as powerful as penicillin.

- **Cinnamon:** A spice plant thought to have antibacterial properties and to be useful against the E.Coli bacteria. When garlic cloves are added, it is supposed to be a very powerful antibiotic.

- **Thyme:** Considered to be a good antiseptic that also stimulates the immune system. It is also good for bacterial skin disorders and as a mouthwash.

WMD Home Preparedness Strategies

The alphabetical list presented here simply gives information about costs and where to locate these suggested items; you should substitute or replace portions of the list as you deem unnecessary or as advised by medical personnel. Keep in mind that you are not trying to establish a mini-pharmacy; rather you are trying to prepare a WMD Kit with basic items just in case it is ever needed. Some items may require a doctor's prescription, but many should be easy to obtain if you explain why you want them. Other items may require a much more diligent search.

Naturally, there are many other sources for these items that may be purchased for less than what we have noted here, and we advise you to locate other such sources. For instance, many medications are cheaper in Mexico and Canada, but medications from Mexico are known to have been mislabeled, or to use substitute medications. In other words, the quality control of medications made in other countries are not to the same standards are those use by our Food and Drug Administration (FDA) and all such purchases should be made with that in mind.

- **Antibiotics:** In most case a doctor's prescription is required; however, some doctors will relent if you explain the purpose for having the medication on hand. The alternative is to wait until it is needed, or to trust your government and health officials to have them in the event of an emergency.

- **Antitoxins:** Most antitoxins are controlled by the government agencies, and the ones we addressed in this document are much more difficult to obtain in the USA.

- **Atropine:** This is the antidote provided to the military and medical EMS personnel for nerve agents. If you decide to obtain this item, please ensure you also get the medical data for use, dosages, and complications with other medications, etc.

Basic Home Items

Protective items for partial protection from NBC agents

- Soap & water (the easiest to find decontaminants)

- Paint drop plastic cloth for doors and windows

- Tarpaulins

- Plastic raincoats

- Ponchos and galoshes, rain hat/hood

- Rubber gloves

- A tube of Elmer's Liquid Glue (available at Home Depot, Wal-Mart, etc.)

- Surgical and gas masks (see below)

- Surgical Gloves

- Baby wipes and Purell or Dial waterless hand sanitizers, etc.

Personal medications

- Basic painkillers: Aspirin, Tylenol
- First aid items: band-aids, Bacitracin, etc.

House Supplies

- Water and water purification tablets
- Bleach (for decontamination - see below)
- Canned and dried foods
- Rugged clothing (Levis, boots, heavy socks, etc.)
- Gas can
- Transistor radio and extra batteries
- Guns and ammo (see below)

Infants, babies, children, and pregnant women

These individuals may require different types of medications or differing dosages; therefore, these medications need to be determined ahead of time to avoid causing more harm than good. Check with your doctor for advice on these special issues.

- **Decontamination items:** Bleach such as Clorox for chemical agents on things and places; hard soaps such as Lava or Boraxo for washing off radiation and chemical agents from the body. Note: Fuels and solvents decontaminate things, not people.

- **Gas Masks:** Surplus gas masks sold in Army/Navy stores are usually old and leak, and they are not recommended. Many items, like up-to-date gas masks and protective clothing, are not normally sold to the general public for reasons we think are questionable at best. However, the Survivair Quick 2000 Mask, used by government agencies, is now available to the public over the Internet. It appears to be a better choice than the surgical masks. Unfortunately, the cost is high, but the mask has a longer lifespan than other masks and is thought to be useful for the prevention of inhaling radioactive dust particles as well as chemical and biological agents. Gas masks from Survivair run $179.95, a practice hood $59.95, and a soft carry pouch $29.95.

- **Radiation Protection:** NORAD is available in most health food stores for $9.95, and is used for internal protection from radiation (Chapter 1 covers its typical use). External protection requires shielding. One source for RAI pills is a website called Radiation-Pills.com http://www.radiation-pills.com/

- **Self-defense protection:** Be aware that people who are normally calm in many stressful situations can become unstable when confronted by an unseen enemy. Weapons and ammunition should be available to protect your family, your friends, and yourself from desperate and unstable people.

- **Surgical Masks:** Surgical masks are available via the Internet and you can purchase them at other medical supply outlets. You get should get the type of surgical mask that is inexpensive and filters out anything below 0.1 microns. This is not the perfect solution, but is better than leaky gas masks, although up-to-date protective clothing and equipment is the preferred safety method.

- **Surgical Gloves:** Surgical gloves are also available via the Internet and you can also purchase these at other medical supply outlets, as with the masks.

- **Water Storage:** You may want to keep three to five large water containers in the garage or basement, as open water may become unavailable or contaminated in case of a WMD event. This water may be required for cooking, drinking, and using for ill or disabled family members or friends. Large discount retailers such as Baja's and Sam's Club sell 5 gallon spring water bottles that you can store for long periods of time.

Staying In Touch With Your Family

In case of any emergency and you happen to become separated from family members — whether prior to, after, or during any emergency — all families should have a prearranged meeting place or location, preferably with a friend or relative far away from your home location, that you can all use to make contact with separated family members.

Instruct your family members to leave any contaminated areas as soon as possible and head directly, if possible, to the prearranged location, because phone and electrical services may be disrupted or become unserviceable.

Appendix - Recommended Websites and Publications

There are literally millions of other sites to visit; however, we think these sites are the most useful to begin your website searches. We found most sites provide guidance for medically trained people, and the military sites are geared more for the military personnel, thus, wording and acronyms would not be familiar to the average civilian layperson.

Government Sites and Publications

- **The Centers for Disease Control and Prevention** www.cdc.gov is in Atlanta, Georgia. Its website provides data on bio-terrorism and is the disease control center for the nation.

- **The Bioterroism Readiness Plan: A Template for Healthcare Facilities** is a downloadable document (.PDF) available from the CDC www.cdc.gov/ncidod/hip/Bio/13apr99APIC-CDCBioterrorism.PDF

- This document was produced by the APIC Bioterrorism Task Force: Judith F. English, Mae Y. Cundiff, John D. Malone, & Jeanne A. Pfeiffer, and the CDC Hospital Infections Program Bioterrorism Working Group: Michael Bell, Lynn Steele, & Michael Miller.

- **The Chemical and Biological Primer** is a 25-page worldview on terrorism with an overview of nuclear/biological/chemical (NBC) warfare, published by the Deputy Assistant to the Secretary of Defense for Bio/Chemical Defense. Some recommended treatments are included. www.defenselink.mil

- **Department of Homeland Security** website www.dhs.gov has a section devoted to **Emergencies & Disasters**, including WMD incidents. www.dhs.gov/dhspublic/display?theme=14&content=292

- **The Federal Emergency Management Agency (FEMA)** is in the Department of Homeland Security. Its website provides information on bio-terrorism and natural disasters. They have an excellent tool kit; unfortunately, for the areas discussed above, they are divided into large sections: Chemical @ 58 pages, Radiological @ 36 pages, and Biological @ 21 pages. www.fema.gov/help/site.shtm

- **"Are You Ready? A Guide to Citizen Preparedness – A Citizen's Protection Guide"** is published by FEMA. You can read the online version at www.fema.gov/areyouready

- **"The Online Emergency Checklist"** and many other online information sources are also available from the FEMA Library www.fema.gov/library

- **The Department of Health and Human Services** website www.hhs.gov has extensive data on a variety of health conditions, including bio-terrorism information. www.governmentguide.com provides links to the Food and Drug Administration (FDA) and the CDC. This site has data on public preparedness and response. www.governmentguide.com

- **The Department of Defense** website www.dod.govl has links to specific areas of interest for Nuclear, Biological, and Chemical warfare, as well as data on bio-terrorism.

- **Guidebook for Marines**, by The Marine Corps Association. (You can see excerpts and ordering information here: www.usmcpress.com/guidebook.htm

Fleet Marine Forces Manuals:

- FMFM 11-2, NBC defense, Chemical Warfare, Smoke and Flame Operation

- FMFM 11-18 Nuclear Contamination Avoidance.

Army Field Manuals:

- FM 3-3 Chemical and Biological Contamination Avoidance

- FM 3-4 Nuclear, Biological, & Chemical (NBC) Protection

- FM 3-5 NBC Decontamination; FM 3-7 NBC Field Handbook

- FM 3-9 Potential Military Chemical/ Biological Agents and Compounds

- FM 4.02.283 Treatment of Nuclear and Radiological Casualties

- FM 8-284 Treatment of Biological Warfare Casualties

- FM 8-285 Treatment of Chemical Agent Casualties and Conventional Military Chemical Injuries.

Non-Profit and Commercial Sites

- The American Herbalists Guild website www.americanherbalistsguild.com provides information on herbs and access to other links. You can email them for information at www.ahgoffice@earthlink.net

- The **American Medical Association** web site www.ama-assn.org has information on disaster preparedness and biological agents.

- **www.emedicine.com** is a world medical library site for various forms of biological and chemical warfare.

- The **Health World Online** web site www.healthy.net/nch provides information on Homeopathy and access to other sites.

- **The Holistic Medicine** organization was founded to unite licensed physicians who practice holistic medicine and to support and educate holistic practitioners.
www.holisticmedicine.org
www.holisticmedicine.org

- **Judicial Watch** is a public interest watchdog group. We urge anyone interested in the subjects of national protection and national defense to purchase or borrow from your local library the book <u>Fatal Neglect</u> by Larry Klayman, Judicial Watch founder, as it covers many other areas about the failure of our government to protect its citizens. <u>www.judicialwatch.org</u>

- **www.mddepot.com** is one of many sites where you can purchase surgical masks and other medical items. This site lists 50 High Performance Isolation Masks that exceed less than .1 microns for $10. This site also sells Latex surgical gloves in quantities of 40 pair for $38.50.

- **The American Association of Naturopathic Physicians** web site <u>www.naturopathic.org</u> provides information and other sites to naturopathic remedies.

- **The National Center for Homeopathy** website <u>www.homeopathic.org</u> has a section on *"Homeopathy Can Help! Flu, Epidemics, trauma, and other health crisis* <u>www.homeopathic.org/crisis.htm</u>

- **www.nbc-links.com** is an excellent site that provides links to numerous government and military sites. It also provides 18 sites relating to civilian organizations and NBC home protection information to include updated data on nuclear, biological, and chemical warfare and agents.

- **www.quackwatch.org** is a site that disputes much of the holistic and alternative medicines theories. Stephen Barrett, M.D. provides answers for your questions and answers. He takes issue with the various home remedies, alternative medications, and what he regards as fraudulent claims.

- **www.redcross.org** is a private emergency response organization. Its web site has data on emergency services in disaster areas, as well as many links to other sites.

- **www.quickmask.com** is a site that sells the Quick200 Chem-Bio-Rad escape hood for protection against these agents.

- **www.webmd.com** is a medical site for facts concerning anthrax, smallpox, etc.

Non-Profit and Commercial Publications[3]

- Biohazard: The Chilling True Story of the Largest Covert Biological Weapons Program in the World, Told by Ken W. Alibek, With Stephen Handelman, Dell Publishing Company, Inc., March 2000, ISBN: 0385334966, Paperback, 336 pp.

- Biological Weapons and America's Secret War-Germs, by Judith Miller, Stephen Engleberg, and William Broad, Simon & Schuster Adult Publishing Group, September 2001. ISBN: 0684871580, Hardcover, 382 pp.

---

[3] We elected not to reference and annotate the various authors, listed and not listed, as much of the information is the same or similar for most reference sites.

- <u>Curing Everyday Ailments the Natural Way</u>, The Reader's Digest Association, Inc., June 2000, SBN: 0762102403, Hardcover, 381 pp.

- <u>Diseases of History</u>, by Fredrick F. Cartwright & Michael D. Biddiss. [May be out of print.]

- <u>EBOLA</u>, by William T. Close, M.D., Meadowlark Springs Production, December 1, 2001; ISBN: 0970337116, Paperback: 396 pp.

- <u>Fatal Neglect</u> by Larry Klayman, Judicial Watch Inc., September 6, 2002, ISBN: 0967943914, Paperback: 199 pp.

- <u>Natural Defenses Against Bioterrorism</u>, by Skye Weintraub, M.D., Woodland Publishing, January 1, 2002; ISBN: 1580543464, Paperback: 46 pp.

- New Webster's Dictionary and Thesaurus & Medical Dictionary, published for Book Essentials by Ottenheimer Publishers, Inc.

- <u>Scourge: The Once and Future Threat of Smallpox</u> by Jonathan B. B. Tucker, Grove/Atlantic, Inc., August 2001, ISBN: 0871138301Hardcover, 291 pp.

- <u>The Hot Zone</u>, by Richard Preston, Ph.D., 1st Anchor Books ed edition, July 20, 1995, ISBN: 0385479565, Mass Market Paperback: 448 pp.

- <u>The Pill Book</u>, 11th Edition, by Harold M. Silverman, Pharm.D, Lawrence D., Chilnick, Bert Stern, & Gilbert I. Simon Sc.D. Bantam Doubleday Dell Publishing Group, April 2004, ISBN: 055338161X, Paperback, 1230 pp.

- The Secret Life of Germs, by Philip M. Tierno, Jr. Ph.D., Atria Books, December 2003, ISBN: 0743421884, Paperback, 320 pp.

- The Way of Herbs, by Michael Tierra, L. Ac., OMD, Simon & Schuster Adult Publishing Group, July 1998, ISBN: 0671023276, Paperback, 416 pp.

- Virus Hunters of the CDC, by Joseph B. McCormick, M.D. and Susan Fisher-Hoch, M.D. , Barnes & Noble Books, August 1999, ISBN: 0760712115, Paperback, 397 pp.

- When Every Moment Counts: What You Need To Know About Bioterrorism From the Senate's Only Doctor by Senator Bill Frist, M.D. , Rowman & Littlefield Publishers, Inc, March 2002, ISBN: 0742522458, Paperback, 192 pp.

- Where There is No Doctor (A Remote Village Health Care Handbook), by David Werner, Carol Thuman and Jane Maxwell, The Hesperian Foundation, May 1998, ISBN: 0942364155, Paperback, 446 pp.

- Yeasts: (How They Cure or Make You Sick), by Dr. William G. Crook, Professional Books (1986), ISBN: 0933478070, 32 pp.

Epilogue

September 26, 2005

Since my writing of the original of the Home Remedies and Protection from WMD agents in 2003, I have added the fiction novel in order to peak the interest of those not so inclined to read through some of the dry reading often filled with medical terms, and protective measures that some now believe are unnecessary. Some will depend on the government to provide the protection from WMD agents and even from Terrorists, although this lack of response capabilities, proper training, and sufficient medications has been written about often enough in the past years, and certainly enough to cause all reasonably thinking people to understand by now that we as a nation remain quite unprepared. We are even now only capable of supporting not much more than a few minor (not major) WMD incidents, or possibly one major hurricane.

Although, we have been warned often enough by Muslim terrorists of pending attacks planned for our nation, we as a people and sadly our own government leaders as well, have taken an attitude of "let them come and we will then deal with it." It is as though we know a Pearl Harbor attack is coming, and rather than prepare, we simply wait for the inevitable like sheep surrounded by wolves and not knowing which direction to run.

As I depicted in my book, on March 23, 2005, there were explosions at a BP refinery in Texas City. At least two Islamic terrorist groups have attempted to take responsibility for these explosions. Later on April 30, 2005, several explosions rocked another Texas City refinery killing 15 and injuring more than 100. Federal investigators believe there were as many as five distinct explosions in rapid succession, with the conclusion that these multiple events were not accidental.

In yet another incident a Middle Eastern man was seen photographing the BASF Corporation ammonia terminal in Freeport. When confronted, he pulled a gun and shot the guard. The gunman was described as dark complexioned with a thick Middle Eastern accent and driving a Chevrolet pickup with no front license plate. Fearing they may be targets in a future attack on chemical plants and refineries, their management had tightened security beginning on September 11, 2001, and has now increased even those security upgrades and measures much more due to the latest and most recent incidents.

In that location, BASF is the second largest producer of ammonium sulfate in the world and their Freeport complex includes 16 plants, including an ammonia plant right next to the Houston deep water cargo port. Ammonia can be explosive when mixed with air, and Law-enforcement sources say that common sense dictates that "terrorism would be everyone's first guess, if inexplicable explosions occurred at that plant". Read Joseph Farah's G2Bulletin account of the event here:

http://www.wnd.com/news/article.asp?ARTICLE_ID=36765

Our leaders seem to want to ignore that Red China is behind many of the terrorist activities, for both business and political reasons. In fact, they have trained many, many of the terrorists throughout the world as have the Cuban military, and yet our leaders behave as though it is better to retain diplomatic and trade relations with our major enemy than to take them to task. That is, rather than to face reality and accept that Red China is the true enemy, or even to acknowledge that their published book titled "Unrestricted Warfare" on how to conquer and subjugate our nation and our people is a part of their overall global plan. It is as though it is simply the fantasy writing of some Red Chinese Army Colonel's, and which is of no real concern at our senior levels of diplomacy. This same attitude of obliviousness existed prior to WWII, when a former Corporal named Adolf Hitler wrote a book titled "Mien Kampf," and the so-called brilliant leaders of that era chose to ignore those writings as well, until it was too late.

The concerns listed second part of this book have now come to pass to some degree with the recent disasters brought about by hurricane Katrina. The death and destruction brought on by this event provided our citizens with but a small sample of what could occur in the event the WMD agents were to be used against our people. Today much finger pointing is being directed at both the Federal as well as the State leaders, that is, for being unprepared for a mere hurricane. As also pointed out in this book, the coordination between Federal, State, and Local agencies and departments was all theoretical in the past, and unbelievably this now includes political judgments, decisions, and considerations, rather than only in the preservation of lives and the safety of our citizens.

The Posse Comitatus Act is a relic of the Civil War era, and was intended to rid the South of Union troops or else keep them on their bases and forts. It was also a pretext for many to enact the infamous "Jim Crow Laws," meant to keep newly freed slaves in their place. This also allowed for State Governor's to be the required authority for allowing Federal Troops to be used in any given State, that is, in case of insurrections, disasters, defense, or any other uses. Theoretically, each State had its own National Guard units to be used under the above conditions. But as recently seen in Louisiana, Mississippi, and Alabama there are not always sufficient numbers to handle all situations.

The Posse Comitatus Act should be rescinded, as under present day conditions there might be little time for a decision consensus in order to obtain State Governor's approval if our nation is attacked in a number of States at almost the same time, or during the same period. As of this writing, the Mayor of New Orleans (State) and the Coast Guard Admiral coordinator (Federal) of the Rescue Units were at odds as to whether people could or should return to New Orleans proper, and the question remains one of who is ultimately in charge! In a crisis or disaster situation, you cannot have more than one boss or leader, or else as shown in this situation the public receives contradictory instructions or orders. This causes even further turmoil and confusion with the citizenry.

I might add the Posse Comitatus Act is used as decided in Washington anyhow, as the Bonus Marchers of WWI were scattered with Federal troops, and George Wallace certainly never called for Federal troops when he attempted to keep black children from entering segregated schools in the late 1950s. Yet they arrived even without his permission! Thus, this Act can be arbitrary, and must be rescinded with a better chain of command structure, and a new law must be initiated for the immediate Federal response to disasters or state/national security, as the present system can work only when authorities have notice and time to react. But in case of an unexpected or an unanticipated WMD incident, then time is of the essence and Governors, Mayors, and the like might not have the time, or the abilities, or the desires to react responsibly as seen under our present system.

By now, many have found fault or will soon find fault with the many Federal, State, and Local Disaster Plans, and these need to be corrected and expanded in order to cover all areas of need that might have been previously overlooked. For instance, New Orleans had a large number of tugboats and fishing boats nearby and available for use during the recent crisis, yet they were never used nor called upon, as they were most likely not even a part of the planning. Likewise, the Governor of Louisiana stated she had not heard from several of her Parishes, and how could that be? Apparently the canned disaster control scenarios never undertook to insure certain emergency radio channels and attendants were on call and in communications on a 24/7 basis. Apparently, few ever heard of satellite communications before this disaster, and hopefully will now consider it as a necessity.

Many Americans do not understand that FEMA was never intended to become a first responder agency per se, but rather was set up as follow on personnel for processing property disaster loans and the like. The do training and help in planning for disaster with local and state agencies, they help locate lost people, and can call on other agencies, groups, and departments for assistance. But in the end, they are but yet another government agency, often more concerned with proper paperwork and the filling out of forms, than in the multiple tasks assigned to them. This agency consists of only approximately 2,262 members, and most are bureaucrats with little in the way of leadership training or experience. Additionally, they have about 4,448 "on call" Disaster Assistant employees; and another 3,278 "on call" Disaster Temporary employees; as well as 703 "Core" employees, who manage the Headquarters and regional offices.

Thus, when called up, FEMA has the ability to provide around 2,900 employees for the entire USA! The problems occur when these individuals and other petty bureaucrats and officials are given authority far beyond their capabilities, and then they tend to abuse the authority given. To believe that the people from FEMA all have the knowledge and abilities to react as leaders in crisis situations is to be both foolhardy and unrealistic. FEMA can call up assets from the Military, CDC, The EPA (HazMat Teams), and other Agencies or Departments, but their command structure remains one of people not knowing one another in many, many cases, and not necessarily all agreeing on given directives or policies.

A military General has troops that obey, and will place anyone under arrest or fire anyone who fails to comply with given orders. That cannot and does not happen under civilian control. While Americans do not want the military running the various state's affairs; in times of panic, chaos, disasters, catastrophes, insurrection, or attacks on our nation-the military must take over to restore order and control, as civilians simply cannot do it except in very limited areas and locations. Furthermore, civilians can quit or leave their jobs at will as seen in New Orleans, thus they are all civilians to include the Police, Fire fighters, and EMT folks, that is, all except for the military

Hopefully, our leaders will now start to do the type of planning that should have been done some 50 years ago. But many who are tasked with these planning assignments are not always the best available, as some are political appointees and others simply enjoy going to endless meetings, and then submitting occasional and minor changes to canned and long ago prepared disaster plans. All senior officials down to city and county council members should review the plans that others have written, and ask questions such as where would we take 12,000 bodies if that situation arose here? Do our hospitals and first responders have the right type of and sufficient quantities of protective gear? Have they been properly trained in the use of this gear and equipment?

Do we have signs prepared in case of an emergency to the hospitals, morgues (such as open fields or stadiums), and water, food, and clothing locations for vehicular traffic? Can we get gas to cars or trucks blocking the roadways due to lack of fuel availability? Should special lanes be set aside for trucks, ambulances, and buses carrying the elderly as well as the evacuees? There are many more questions to ask and this is but a small example. But for those who have chosen to take on the titles of authority, whether elected or appointed, they then should also be responsible for double checking the planning of their subordinates, and they should be tasked with responsibility and with the concurrence of all disaster plans under their control.

We have a number of enemies seeking to destroy our nation and our way of life. They are: the Red Chinese, the Radical Islamists, the soon to surface Latino Terrorists, as well as many within our own nation. They are certainly coming, as they have stated it publicly and even written books on their intentions and goals.

We had better become prepared to give up many of our rights as was done in WWII, and to be prepared to incarcerate or relocate many of our fellow citizens. When the nation's safety is at stake, then we will all have to adjust to that which will preserve our nation and our people, or we will surely become subjugated and slaves of one or a combination of the above enemy forces.

Major Frank C. Stolz, USMC (Ret)

26 September, 2005

www.WMDTerror.com

Printed in the United States
50653LVS00001B/73-105